THE ENGLISH YOU NEED FOR THE OFFICE

Susan Dean and Lawrence J. Zwier

MULTI-SKILLS ACTIVITY BOOK

Asia-Pacific Press Holdings Ltd.

Asia-Pacific Press Holdings Ltd.
22nd Floor, Lane Crawford House
70 Queen's Road Central, Hong Kong

Distributed by:
Falcon Press Sdn Bhd, Malaysia
Tel: 03-77812303, 03-77812308
Fax: 03-77812312
E-mail: falconp@po.jaring.my
Website: www.falconpub.com

The English You Need for the Office
A Picture Process Vocabulary Multi-Skills Activity Book

Susan Dean and Lawrence J. Zwier

© Asia Pacific Press Holdings Ltd, Hong Kong, 2003
10 9 8 7 6 5 4 3 2 1
07 06 05 04 03

ISBN 962 328 020 3

Printed by Shinhwa, Korea

Contents

To the Teacher

The activities in this book will help your students work with the vocabulary from the main text of *The English You Need for the Office* (EYNO). These activities encourage students to remember what they have learned and to exercise their personal networks of picture-word or word-word associations.

The exercises in each chapter address both the written and spoken forms of the vocabulary.

Organization

Each chaper of the multi-skills activity book corresponds to a chapter in the main text of *EYNO*. In addition, there is a two-page set of review exercises at the end of each section. These review exercises integrate the vocabulary from all the chapters of the section and help students build connections among them. At the end of the multi-skills activity book is a complete answer key.

Activity Types

Each multi-skills activity book chapter begins with an activity to help exercise a student's picture-word associations. This is followed by an activity—often a matching exercise—to help students remember meanings, collocations, or other important features surrounding the written form of the language. Finally, each chapter contains a listening exercise to help students work with the spoken forms of the key vocabulary.

The review sections involve a wide variety of exercises—matching, grouping, collocating, associating words with pictures—for both the written and spoken forms.

The exercises in this multi-skills activity book are suitable even for students who have limited productive abilities in English. The student does not have to be able to write or speak very well in order to complete them. We have done this deliberately so that even low-production students can enhance their vocabularies—with the eventual goal of greater production.

If your students are more advanced in their productive abilities, you may want to modify the presentation of these activities. For example, in the pictorial sections, you could use each picture as stimulus for a larger writing activity. The multi-skills activity book asks students only to fill in a blank. You could go further and ask your students to write fuller descriptions of what they see, or to number the pictures in the order of their occurrence in real life, or to invent dialogues to accompany the pictures.

Please also remember that, at the back of the main text of *EYNO*, there are photocopiable templates of process pages. Students can use these to describe the processes they go through in their own lives.

We hope this multi-skills activity book can enhance your students' work with *The English You Need for the Office*.

To the Student

This multi-skills activity book will help you remember and use the vocabulary you learned in the main text of *The English You Need for the Office (EYNO)*. These activities involve reading, writing, and listening.

Organization
Each chapter in this book goes with a chapter in the main text. Also, there are some extra activities at the end of each section. A complete answer key is at the back of the book.

How to Use this Book
You can do these exercises in a class or by yourself. If you are working by yourself, use the answer key to check your work.

Before you start the exercise for a chapter, review the chapter with the same number of *EYNO*. Once you have finished all the chapters in a section, do the review exercises at the end of a section. This will help you remember a wider range of vocabulary.

We hope you learn a lot from the main text and these exercises. Enjoy using the new vocabulary you have learned!

1. Getting Ready for Work

A. **Filling in**. Fill in each blank with the best word or phrase from the list. Do not use any item more than once.

getting dressed   making   packing   putting on   shutting   watching

1. Matt is _____ a jacket.

2. He is _____ a news program.

3. He is _____ .

4. Matt is _____ breakfast.

5. He is _____ a lunch.

6. He is _____ the door as he leaves.

B. **Matching**. Match each word with the best definition or description. Write the letter in the blank. Do not use any letter more than once.

_____	1. a closet	a.	used to make clothes smooth
_____	2. a blouse	b.	look at something quickly
_____	3. check	c.	place where clothing may be kept
_____	4. loafers	d.	take something quickly
_____	5. grab	e.	type of shirt
_____	6. an iron	f.	casual shoes

C. **Listening**. Listen to the tape/CD and circle the best word or phrase to complete each statement.

1. lunch / briefcase / newspaper
2. a brown bag / his briefcase / some cereal
3. casual clothes / dress clothes
4. casual clothes / dress clothes
5. muffins / loafers / laundry
6. a bed / a shower / an alarm clock

1

2. Arriving at the Office

A. **Filling in**. *Fill in each blank with the best word or phrase from the list. Do not use any item more than once.*

entering
going through

hanging
making small talk

parking
taking

unlocking
walking

1. Tina is _____ her car.

2. She is _____ down the hall.

3. She is _____ with her coworkers.

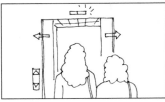

4. She is _____ an elevator to her floor.

5. She is _____ her coat on a rack.

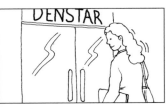

6. She is _____ the building.

7. She is _____ security.

8. She is _____ her door.

B. **Filling in**. *Fill each blank with the name of what it points to:* parking lot, hall, building, office cubicle

1. _____

2. _____

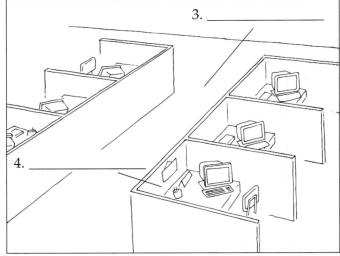

3. _____

4. _____

C. **Listening**. *Listen to the tape/CD and circle the best word or phrase to complete each statement.*

1. a door / a floor

2. an elevator / a lobby

3. a briefcase / a key

4. coworkers / car

5. her briefcase / a security guard

6. a building / a parking lot

2

3. Going through Security

A. *Filling in*. Fill in each blank with the best word or phrase from the list. Do not use any item more than once.

checking entering identifying letting restricted temporary pass

1. Alice is _____ her access code.

2. The guards are not _____ Albert in.

Sorry, sir. No one enters without an ID.

3. The guards are _____ Tina's badge.

4. The guards are giving Albert a _____ .

5. This is a _____ area.

AUTHORIZED PERSONNEL ONLY

6. Ms. Perez is _____ Albert.

Yes. This is Albert Turner.

B. Choose the best word from the list below to complete each informal definition. Write the word in the blank.

badge ID number recognize wave

1. When you _____ , you move your hand.
2. "_____" is a short form of "identification."
3. A _____ is a kind of ID.
4. When you _____ someone, you know who they are.
5. Alice's access code is a _____ .

C. *Listening*. Listen to the tape/CD. For each statement or question you hear, write the letter of the best response in the blank. Do not use the same letter more than once.

1. _____
2. _____
3. _____
4. _____
5. _____
6. _____

a. But I forgot it. Please let me in.
b. Good morning, Ms Perez.
c. The shipping department.
d. Thanks.
e. Yes. He works for me.
f. I won't forget it again.

4. Reporting for Work

A. *Under each picture write the name of the best description from the list.*

moving something   punching in   putting something in   writing in a time

  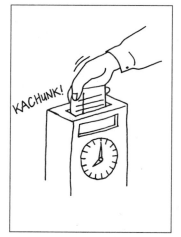 

1. _____   2. _____   3. _____   4. _____

_____   _____   _____   _____

B. **Filling in.** *Fill in each blank with a verb from the list. Do not use any verb more than once.*

check   moved   opened   printed   punched in   showed   took   wrote in

1. The in/out board _____ that Kay was out.

2. Albert _____ his time card from the rack.

3. Matt _____ his marker to the "in" column.

4. Alice _____ the sign-in book to today's page.

5. Alice wrote her name. Then she _____ the time.

6. What time is it? I don't know. _____ the clock.

7. Albert put his card in the time clock and _____.

8. The machine _____ the date and time on his card.

C. **Listening.** *Listen to the tape/CD and circle the word or phrase that is part of what the speaker says.*

1. wrote in / was in / punched in

2. wrote in / was in / punched in

3. the board / the book / the clock

4. the clock / time clock / the rack

5. printed / checked / put in

6. opened / back in / showed

7. column / clock / found

8. date / name / page

4

5. Getting Settled at the Office

A. **Matching**. *Match each word with the best definition. Write the letter in the blank.*
   Do not use any letter more than once.

_____	1. bag lunch	a.	something to carry papers in
_____	2. hook	b.	a room where you hang things
_____	3. refrigerator	c.	a room where you can eat
_____	4. briefcase	d.	you bring this from home to eat at work
_____	5. coat room	e.	this is attached to a wall; you hang things on it
_____	6. lunch room	f.	this keeps things cold

B. **Filling in**. *Fill in each blank with the best word or phrase from the list.*
   Some items may be used more than once.

at   from   in   on   to

1. Matt sat down _____ his desk.
2. He set his briefcase _____ the desk.
3. I put my lunch _____ the refrigerator.

4. Sue took some papers _____ her briefcase.
5. Jim looked _____ pictures of his kids.
6. Lefty took some coffee back _____ his desk.

C. **Listening**. *Listen to the tape/CD. Write the number of each description below the picture that best matches it.*

a. _____   b. _____   c. _____   d. _____

e. _____   f. _____   g. _____   h. _____

6. Planning Your Day/Scheduling

A. *Under each picture, write the best caption from the list.*

| date book | desk calendar | electronic organizer | to-do list |

1. _____ 2. _____ 3. _____ 4. _____

B. *Cross out one item from each of the following groups – the item that does not fit with the others. Use the "hint" at the right to help you decide.*

Example: dog, horse, bird, ~~cat~~   Hint: animals

1. calendar, appointment book, diary, software   Hint: other names for "date book"
2. date book, PDA, palmtop, electronic organizer   Hint: names for a small computer
3. cancel, call, reschedule, find out   Hint: "_____ a meeting"
4. free slots, open time periods, conflicts, openings   Hint: when you have no meetings

C. **Listening**. *Listen to the tape/CD and circle the best word or phrase to complete each statement below.*

1. She _____ at noon.
   (is free, has an appointment, canceled an appointment)

2. He _____ the dinner.
   (penciled in, checked, rescheduled)

3. She has a _____ .
   (task, schedule conflict, free slot)

4. He's trying to _____ a meeting.
   (write in, call, reschedule)

7. Checking Voicemail Messages

A. **Filling in**. *Fill in each blank with the best word or phrase from the list. Do not use any item more than once.*

entering   hanging up   listening to   picking up   pressing   writing

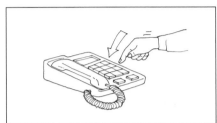

1. Alice is _____ the receiver.

2. She is _____ her PIN.

3. She is _____ the star key.

4. Albert is _____ a message.

5. He is _____ some information.

6. He is _____ the phone.

B. **Matching**. *Match each word with the best definition or description. Write the letter in the blank. Do not use any letter more than once.*

_____	1. blink	a.	a special identification number
_____	2. play	b.	a button on a telephone
_____	3. PIN	c.	to go on and off quickly
_____	4. message	d.	to put information into something
_____	5. key	e.	information given from one person to another
_____	6. enter	f.	to turn on to listen to

C. **Listening**. *Listen to the tape/CD and circle the best word or phrase to complete each statement.*

1. saved it / deleted it / missed it
2. deleted it / pushed it / replayed it
3. pressed it / saved it / entered it
4. missed the beginning / finished it / deleted it
5. entered his PIN / exited voicemail / checked his voicemail
6. hung up the phone / finished the call / wrote down the caller's name

8. Taking a Coffee Break

A. **Matching**. Match each picture with its description. Write the letter in the blank. Do not use any letter more than once.

_____ 1. sharing a snack

_____ 2. going into a break room

_____ 3. using a vending machine

_____ 4. pouring a cup of coffee

_____ 5. leaving a break room

_____ 6. making tea

B. **Filling in**. Fill in each blank with the best word or phrase from the list. Do not use any word more than once.

bin   break room   change   coin slot   notice   up

1. Matt and Albert read a _____ on the bulletin board.

2. At 9:00, Alice went to the _____ for coffee.

3. Matt put some money into the _____ .

4. Matt took his _____ out of the coin return.

5. He removed his chips from the _____ .

6. When break time was _____ , they returned to work.

C. **Listening**. Listen to the tape/CD. Circle the description of the activity each speaker is involved in.

1. offering a snack / making small talk / making tea

2. looking at a bulletin board / making small talk / making coffee

3. making tea / counting out money / opening a bag of snacks

4. looking at a watch / looking at a bulletin board / looking at a vending machine

5. looking at a vending machine / looking at a newspaper / looking at a bulletin board

6. reading the newspaper / making small talk / returning to work

9. Eating Lunch in a Cafeteria

A. **Matching**. Match each word with the best definition or description. Write the letter in the blank. Do not use any letter more than once.

_____	1. portion	a. don't have
_____	2. instead	b. person who prepares and/or gives food
_____	3. menu	c. piece or part of
_____	4. out of	d. person who receives payment
_____	5. cashier	e. in place of something
_____	6. server	f. list of food available in a restaurant

B. For each list, cross out the one item that doesn't fit the description.

1. parts of a cafeteria: salad bar, dining area, tray return, security, steam table

2. items in a salad: tomatoes, lettuce, tongs, croutons, broccoli

3. silverware: knife, napkin, fork, spoon

4. things on a steam table: soup, chicken, fish, lettuce

5. people in a cafeteria: security guard, server, diner, cashier

C. **Listening**. Listen to the tape/CD. Write the number of each description next to the picture that best matches it.

a. _____   b. _____   c. _____   d. _____

e. _____   f. _____   g. _____   h. _____

9

10. Eating a Bag Lunch

A. *Matching*. Match each word with the best definition or description. Write the letter in the blank.
Do not use any letter more than once.

_____ 1. timer

_____ 2. fast food

_____ 3. leftovers

_____ 4. lid

_____ 5. wrapper

_____ 6. bag lunch

a. cover of a container

b. food remaining after a meal

c. piece of paper or plastic covering something

d. meal prepared at home to be eaten somewhere else

e. food cooked quickly and often eaten away from the restaurant where it was prepared

f. something that controls how long a machine is on

B. *Change each of the descriptions below to make it correctly describe the picture above it.*

1. Alice put the container in the microwave.

_____

_____

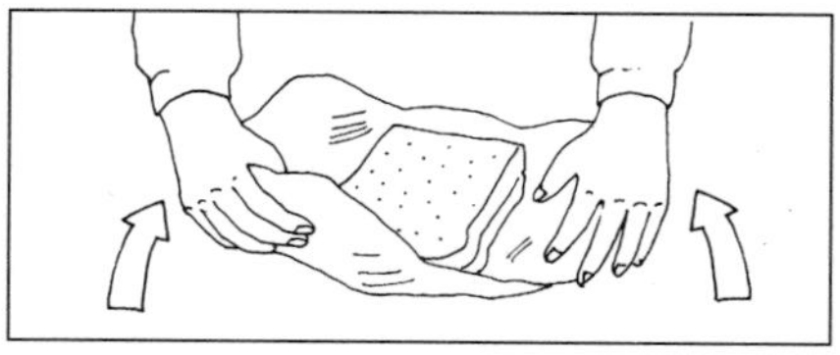

2. Matt unwrapped his sandwich.

_____

_____

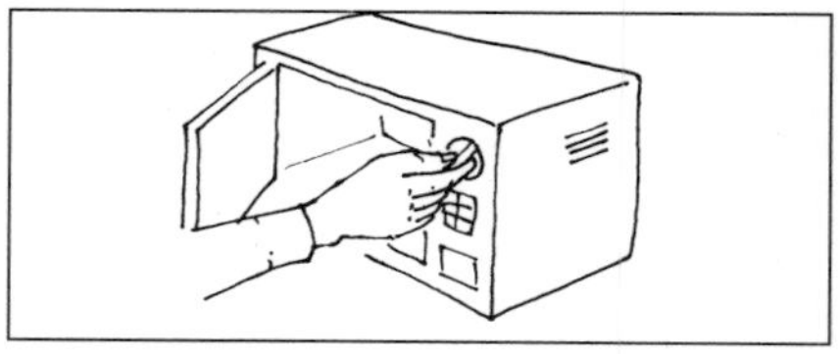

3. Alice set the latch on the microwave.

_____

_____

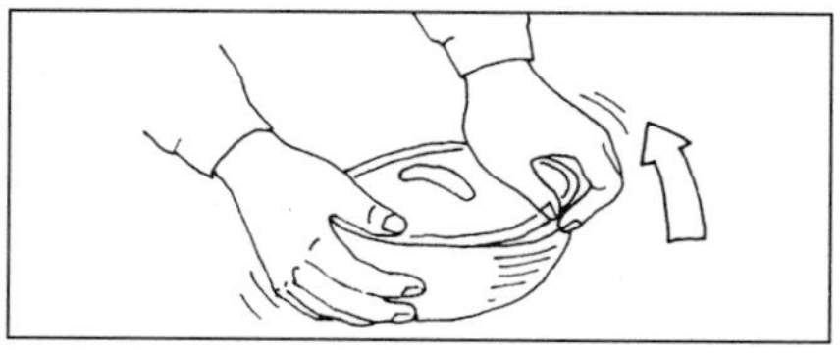

4. Alice closed her container.

_____

_____

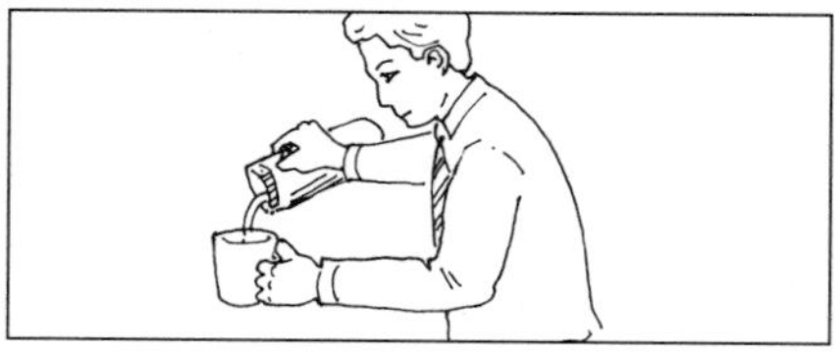

5. Matt sipped some tea from his vacuum bottle.

_____

_____

6. Matt took a bite of his soup.

_____

_____

C. *Listening*. Listen to the tape/CD and circle the best word or phrase to complete each statement.

1. refrigerator / microwave / wrapper

2. refrigerator / microwave / container

3. vacuum bottle / soup / soda

4. wrapped it up / threw it away / removed the twist tie

5. container / soda / bag lunch

6. loosened the lid / crumpled her wrapper / removed the twist tie

11. Spending Lunchtime in Other Ways

A. **Filling in**. Fill in each blank with the best word or phrase from the list. Do not use any item more than once.

cards   cigarette   errands   gym   locker room   tip

1. Tina and Alice wanted to work out so they went to the _____ .
2. Albert didn't eat lunch because he had to run _____ .
3. After lunch, everyone gave money for the bill and the _____ .
4. Before working out, Alice changed clothes in the _____ .
5. Tina and Matt like to play _____ during lunch.
6. During lunch, Matt goes to the smoking area to have a _____ .

B. **Matching**. Match each picture with its description. Write the letter in the blank. Do not use any letter more than once.

a. eating out

b. getting some sun

c. putting on sneakers

d. taking a walk

e. working out

f. running errands

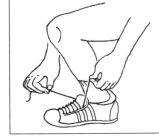

First I'll go to the bank, then the market.

1. _____   2. _____   3. _____

4. _____   5. _____   6. _____

C. **Listening**. Listen to the tape/CD. Circle the description of the activity each speaker is involved in.

1. paying a bill / ordering lunch / playing cards
2. mailing a package / shopping / going to the bank
3. shopping / making a personal call / ordering lunch
4. mailing a package / going to the bank / shopping
5. using exercise equipment / playing cards / reading
6. going to the bank / shopping / playing cards

12. Ending the Workday

A. **Filling in.** Fill in each blank with the best word or phrase from the list. Do not use any item more than once.

crossing off   locking   printing   putting   returning   turning off

1. Alice is _____ a document.

2. Albert is _____ an item on his list.

3. Alice is _____ some papers in her briefcase.

4. Alice is _____ a file to the filing cabinet.

5. She is _____ her desk drawer.

6. Alice is _____ the lights as she leaves.

B. **Matching.** Match each word or phrase with the best definition or description. Write the letter in the blank. Do not use any letter more than once.

_____ 1. deadline   a. turn off

_____ 2. to-do list   b. run water inside something to clean it

_____ 3. late   c. make neater

_____ 4. shut off   d. day or time by which something must be done

_____ 5. straighten   e. after the expected or usual time

_____ 6. rinse out   f. group of things that must be done

C. **Listening.** Listen to the tape/CD and circle the word or phrase that is part of what the speaker says.

1. signed out / shut off / crossed off

2. crossed off / locked / looked at

3. drawer / briefcase / file

4. computer / lights / coffee maker

5. locked / looked at / left

12

13. Leaving the Office

A. **Matching**. *Match each word with the best definition or description. Write the letter in the blank.*
Do not use any letter more than once.

_____	1. column	a. tells the time
_____	2. row	b. tells the time and prints on a time card
_____	3. time clock	c. the "up-down" part of a chart
_____	4. clock	d. the "side-to-side" part of a chart
_____	5. rack	e. a different person
_____	6. someone else	f. a place that holds cards

B. **Filling in.** *Fill in each blank with the best word from the list. Do not use any word more than once.*

moving	putting	setting	writing

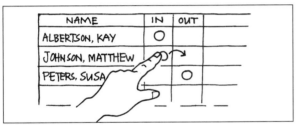

1. He is _____ his marker
   into the "out" column.

2. He is _____ in the
   sign-in book.

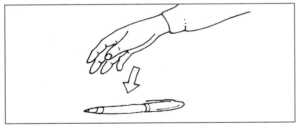

3. She is _____ the pen down.

4. He is _____ his card back
   into the rack.

C. **Listening**. *Listen to the tape/CD and circle the word or phrase that is part of what the speaker says.*

1. took / book
2. signed out / signed in
3. out / found
4. time / sign
5. card / board
6. line / sign

A. *Cross out the one item in parentheses ( ) that does not fit well with the underlined verb.*

1. People can <u>make</u> (small talk, breakfast, their names, a list).

2. People can <u>check</u> (a clock, a guard, a calendar, some sun).

3. People can <u>turn on</u> (a computer, a light, a PIN).

4. People can <u>take</u> (a shower, a break, some small talk, an elevator).

5. People can <u>sip</u> (coffee, a meal, a beverage).

6. People can <u>use</u> (exercise equipment, the restroom, swimming).

7. People can <u>get</u> (some sun, dressed, out of bed, good morning).

B. *Fill in each blank with the best word from the list to complete each description. Do not use any word more than once.*

entering   making   ordering   packing   pressing   putting   signing   taking   writing

1. She is _____ food.

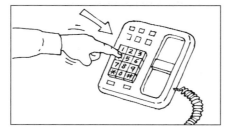

2. He is _____ his PIN.

3. She is _____ the button.

4. He is _____ his card into the slot.

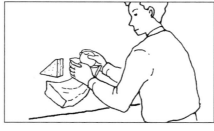

5. Someone is _____ a lunch.

6. They are _____ an elevator.

7. She is _____ in the time.

8. He is _____ a to-do list.

9. He is _____ out.

C. *Match each item in Column A with the best meaning or description from Column B.*
   Write the letter in the blank. Do not use any letter more than once.

Column A	Column B
_____ 1. a pass	a. to take hold of something quickly
_____ 2. to delete something	b. to run water over or through something, to clean it out
_____ 3. to grab something	c. a piece of paper that lets you get into a place
_____ 4. to rinse something	d. one level of a building
_____ 5. a courier	e. to put things in their proper places
_____ 6. temporary	f. the money left over and returned to you after you buy something
_____ 7. a floor	g. a person who delivers letters or packages
_____ 8. to check a clock	h. to remove something
_____ 9. to arrange things	i. to look quickly at it, to find out the time
_____ 10. change	j. for only a short time

D. *Listen to the tape/CD and circle the item which best completes the statement.*

1. Their break is up. / They are reporting for work. / They are making small talk.

2. identify her / forget her / recognize her

3. dropping something off / picking something up / hanging something up

4. checking a calendar / making small talk / saying goodbye

5. counting / penciling something in / ringing something up

6. eating a snack at her desk / going to the bank / ordering something

14. Taking Directions

A. **Matching**. *Match each word or phrase with the best definition or description. Write the letter in the blank. Do not use any letter more than once.*

_____	1. supervisor	a.	things needed to complete a job
_____	2. make sure	b.	small piece of information or a fact
_____	3. materials	c.	give something attention
_____	4. task	d.	job
_____	5. detail	e.	check to be certain you understand
_____	6. highlight	f.	person in charge; boss

B. **Filling in**. *Fill in each blank with the best word or phrase from the list.*

deadline   files   highlighted   nodded

1. Alice's supervisor explained the assignment and gave her the _____ she needed.
2. Alice made sure of the _____ and then wrote it down in her daily planner.
3. Alice understood the details so she _____ as she listened.
4. Her supervisor _____ some important parts of the assignment.

C. **Listening**. *Listen to the tape/CD. Write the number of each description below the picture that best matches it.*

a. _____

b. _____

c. _____

d. _____

e. _____

f. _____

15. Reporting Progress or Problems

A. **Filling in**. Fill in each blank with the best word or phrase from the list.
Do not use any word more than once.

estimating   explaining   left   meeting   pointing   progress

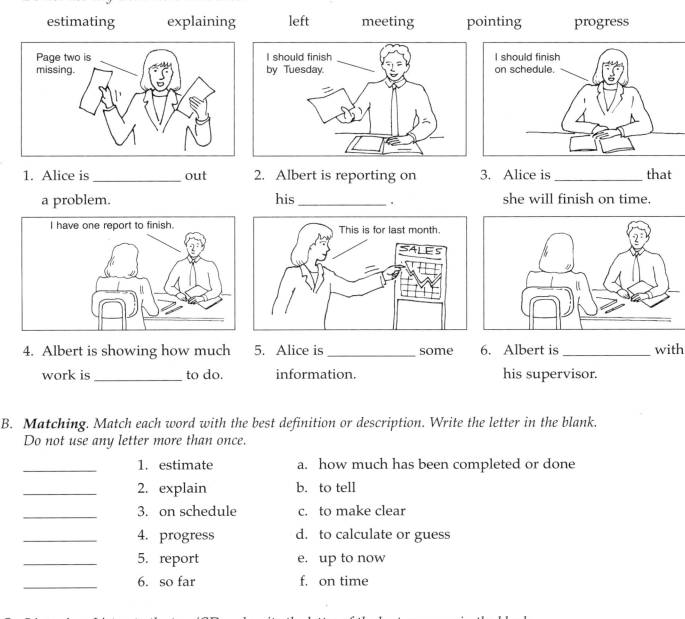

1. Alice is _____ out a problem.

2. Albert is reporting on his _____ .

3. Alice is _____ that she will finish on time.

4. Albert is showing how much work is _____ to do.

5. Alice is _____ some information.

6. Albert is _____ with his supervisor.

B. **Matching**. Match each word with the best definition or description. Write the letter in the blank.
Do not use any letter more than once.

_____   1. estimate   a. how much has been completed or done
_____   2. explain   b. to tell
_____   3. on schedule   c. to make clear
_____   4. progress   d. to calculate or guess
_____   5. report   e. up to now
_____   6. so far   f. on time

C. **Listening**. Listen to the tape/CD and write the letter of the best response in the blank.
Do not use any letter more than once.

1. _____   a. It's going well.
2. _____   b. Yes. It won't be a problem.
3. _____   c. Tuesday.
4. _____   d. This one.
5. _____   e. I'll call Alice for help.

16. Attending a Meeting

A. **Filling in.** *Fill in each blank with the best word or phrase from the list. Do not use any item more than once.*

distributing   giving   making   taking   taking up   thanking

1. He is _____ the first agenda item.

2. She is _____ minutes.

3. He is _____ people for their attention.

4. He is _____ an announcement.

5. She is _____ copies.

6. She is _____ a presentation.

B. **Matching.** *Match each word or phrase with the best definition or description. Write the letter in the blank. Do not use any letter more than once.*

_____ 1. head of the table

_____ 2. participant

_____ 3. taking the floor

_____ 4. whispering

_____ 5. doodling

_____ 6. taking notes

a. writing short points about things you want to remember

b. becoming the person who talks to all the other people at a meeting

c. one end of a table

d. speaking very quietly

e. someone who is involved in a meeting

f. drawing little things to keep yourself busy

C. **Listening.** *Listen to the tape/CD. Circle the description of the activity each speaker is involved in.*

1. opening a meeting / closing a meeting

2. thanking people / moving on to the next item

3. taking up the first item of business / moving on to the next item

4. discussing something / approving minutes

5. giving a presentation / giving someone the floor

17. Taking Minutes

A. *Matching*. *Match each picture with its description. Write the letter in the blank. Do not use any letter more than once.*

a. approving minutes
b. asking someone to repeat
c. making corrections

d. noting the time
e. recording remarks
f. saying something off the record

g. typing the minutes
h. writing down names of participants

1. _____

2. _____

3. _____

4. _____

5. _____

6. _____

7. _____

8. _____

B. *Filling in*. *Fill in each blank with the best word or phrase from the list. Do not use any item more than once.*

amend   minutes   off the record   record   remarks   summarize

1. When you _____ , you write down the main ideas.

2. Something that is _____ is not meant to be a part of the official document.

3. If you _____ something, it means you change it.

4. _____ of a meeting report what was said and done at the meeting.

5. When you _____ something, you write it down.

6. _____ are things that are said or spoken.

C. *Listening*. *Listen to what each speaker at the meeting says. In the blank, write the letter of the activity he or she is performing.*

1. _____

2. _____

3. _____

4. _____

5. _____

a. approving minutes

b. asking someone to repeat something

c. making corrections

d. noting the time

e. saying something off the record

18. Writing a Memo

A. **Filling in**. *Fill in each blank with the best word or phrase from the list. Do not use any item more than once.*

distributing   opening   printing out   proofreading   showing   typing up

1. Matt is _____ his word processing software.

2. He is _____ a memo.

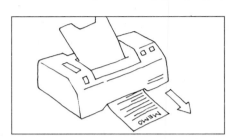

3. The memo is _____ .

4. Matt is _____ the memo.

5. He is _____ the memo to his supervisor.

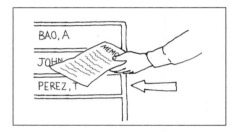

6. He is _____ the memo.

B. *Label the parts of the memo by writing the best item from the list in each box.*

body
date
recipient list
sender's name
subject
typist's initials

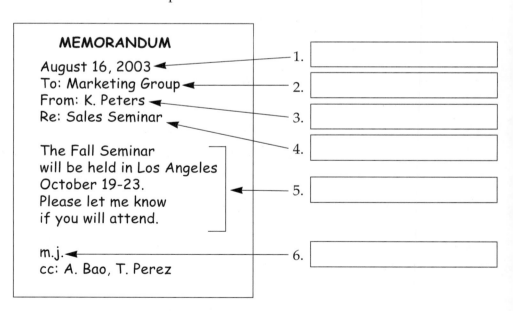

1. _____

2. _____

3. _____

4. _____

5. _____

6. _____

C. **Listening**. *Listen to the tape/CD and circle the best word or phrase to complete each statement.*

1. printer / initials / software

2. mistakes / copies / dates

3. the date / the subject / her initials

4. distributed it / printed it / typed it

20

19. Leaving an Informal Note

A. **Matching**. Match each word with the best definition or description. Write the letter in the blank.
Do not use any letter more than once.

_____	1. jot down	a.	not present; gone
_____	2. pad	b.	write quickly
_____	3. stick	c.	attach or fix
_____	4. peel	d.	remove; tear off
_____	5. be away	e.	casual
_____	6. informal	f.	pieces of paper joined together

B. **Filling in**. Fill in each blank with the best word or phrase from the list.
Do not use any word more than once.

    away   initials   message   self-adhesive

1. Matt signed his _____ on the note, not his full name.

2. Alice was not in her office. She was _____ .

3. Matt used a _____ pad so the paper would stick to Alice's file.

4. He wrote a quick _____ for Alice.

C. **Listening**. Listen to the tape/CD. Write the number of each description below the picture that best matches it.

a. _____   b. _____   c. _____

d. _____   e. _____   f. _____

A. *Cross out the one item in parentheses ( ) that does not fit well with the underlined verb.*
   The first one is done for you as an example.

1. You can <u>open</u> (~~the time~~, software, a meeting).

2. You can <u>write down</u> (people's names, the floor, what people say, a date).

3. You can <u>make</u> (copies, an announcement, corrections, a message).

4. You can <u>take</u> (minutes, notes, the last meeting, the floor).

5. You can <u>give</u> (materials to someone, a presentation, an assignment to someone, a coworker for help).

6. You can <u>type</u> (a memo, a supervisor, some minutes, some notes).

7. You can <u>pick up</u> (the first item of business, a pen, a notepad, a copy of the minutes).

B. *Fill in each blank with the best word or phrase from the list to complete each description.*
   Do not use any item more than once

explaining
nodding
peeling
pointing out
reporting
typing
yawning

1. She is _____ as she listens.

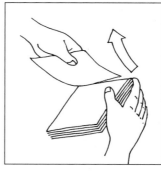

2. He is _____ a piece of paper off the pad.

3. She is _____ up the minutes.

The first part is finished...

4. He is _____ on his progress.

Matt, I need a sales report...

5. The supervisor is _____ a new assignment.

You can't put this figure...

6. He is _____ a problem.

7. She is _____ .

22

C. *Match each item in Column A with the best meaning or description from Column B.*
   Write the letter in the blank. Do not use any item more than once.

	Column A		Column B
_____	1. to proofread	a.	to speak very softly and quietly
_____	2. to summarize	b.	someone who receives something
_____	3. to take some-thing up	c.	to write or say the main ideas of something in fewer words
_____	4. to approve	d.	not to be part of the official report of a meeting
_____	5. a detail	e.	a fact or a small piece of information
_____	6. to whisper	f.	to be gone for a short time
_____	7. a deadline	g.	the date or time when something must be finished
_____	8. a recipient	h.	to say something is okay
_____	9. off the record	i.	to check a document for mistakes
_____	10. to be away	j.	to begin to talk about something, like an item of business

D. *Listen to the tape/CD and circle the item which best completes the statement.*

1. estimating / proofreading / making sure of details

2. closing a meeting / giving a presentation / opening a meeting

3. approving something / discussing something / summarizing something

4. doodling / yawning / whispering

5. giving instructions / approving something / thanking people

6. explaining an assignment / making sure of details / reporting on progress

20. Making Photocopies

A. **Matching**. *Match each word or phrase with the best definition or description. Write the letter in the blank. Do not use any letter more than once.*

_____	1. feeding something in
_____	2. aligning something
_____	3. original
_____	4. adjusting something
_____	5. document
_____	6. reducing something

a. the thing you want to copy

b. a written thing

c. moving something into the right position so it matches properly against a line

d. putting something in, so it can be stored or worked on

e. making changes to something so it is better than before

f. making something smaller

B. **Filling in**. *Fill in each blank with the best word or phrase from the list. Do not use any item more than once.*

| cleared | crosswise | face-down | face-up | multi-page | sorted |

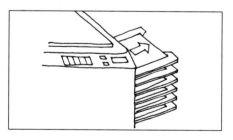

1. This paper is _____ .

2. These sticks are stacked

_____ .

3. This paper is _____ .

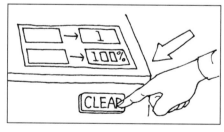

4. These papers are being

_____ .

5. These settings have been

_____ .

6. This is a _____

document.

C. **Listening**. *Listen to the tape/CD. What does the word "it" refer to in each statement? Circle the answer.*

1. lid / photocopier / settings

2. feeder / darkness / size

3. original / settings / button

4. glass / document / tray

21. Dealing with Photocopier Problems

A. **Filling in.** Fill in each blank with the best word from the list. Do not use any item more than once.

broke   pulling   putting   reaching   see   working

1. He is _____ out a
   jammed sheet.

2. She's _____ a sign
   on the machine.

3. She can't _____ one
   of the jammed sheets.

4. He is _____ on the
   machine.

5. The machine _____
   down completely.

6. She is _____ inside
   the machine.

B. For each list, cross out the one item that does not fit the description.

1. Parts of a photocopier: knobs, rollers, paper, glass, jam
2. Things displays say: "clear paper jam", "ready", "it's running now"
3. Things you put into a copier: a sign, toner, paper, toolboxes
4. Photocopier problems: paper jam, smudges on glass, being out of toner, reaching inside

C. **Listening.** Listen to the tape/CD. Put a check mark (✓) next to the best way of completing what the speaker has said.

1. _____ is jammed   _____ works again
2. _____ the display   _____ glass
3. _____ clean it   _____ repair it
4. _____ add toner   _____ turn a knob

25

22. Collating and Stapling

A. **Matching**. *Match each picture with its description. Write the letter in the blank. Do not use any letter more than once.*

_____ 1. The papers are in order.

_____ 2. The stapler is empty.

_____ 3. There are extras of some pages.

_____ 4. The staple went in wrong.

_____ 5. The sets are stacked crosswise.

_____ 6. He's slipping a set into the stapler.

a.

b.

c.

d.

e.

f.

B. **Filling in**. *Fill in each blank with the best item from the list to complete the sentence.*

laid out   on top of   out of   upper right

1. I _____ some pages _____ on a table.

2. I ran _____ _____ some pages.

3. I stapled the pages in the _____ _____-hand corner.

4. I put one sheet _____ _____ _____ another.

C. **Listening**. *Listen to the tape/CD and circle the best way of completing the statement.*

1. remove it / reload it / staple it

2. put one on top of another / lay them out / grab them

3. counting sets / licking his fingers / being in order

4. lick them / count them / stack them

23. Keeping Pages Together/Punching & Binding

A. **Matching**. *Match each word with the best definition or description. Write the letter in the blank. Do not use any letter more than once.*

_____ 1. ribbon   a. you use this to clip things together

_____ 2. a punch   b. these stretch to go around a set of pages

_____ 3. a folder   c. you can bundle things with this; it's thinner than a ribbon

_____ 4. paper clip   d. you can bundle things with this; it's wider than string

_____ 5. rubber bands   e. you can put papers inside this

_____ 6. string   f. you can make holes with this

B. **Filling in.** *Fill in each blank with the best word or phrase from the list. Do not use any item more than once.*

aligning   emptying   side-stapling   slipping

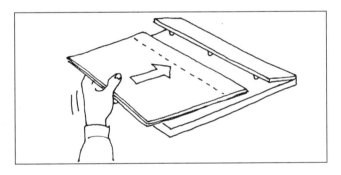

1. He's _____ papers in the punch.

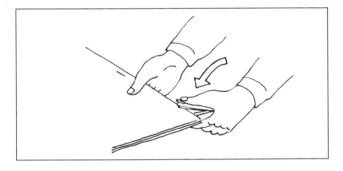

2. He's _____ the pages.

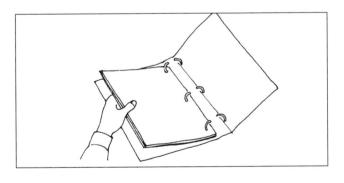

3. He's _____ some pages onto the rings.

4. He's _____ out the scraps.

C. **Listening**. *Listen to the tape/CD and circle the word or phrase that is part of what the speaker says.*

1. three holes / staple / three-ring

2. ribbon / rubber / together

3. press / edge / punch

4. binder / string / spine

24. Filing Documents

A. **Matching**. *Match each picture with its description. Write the letter in the blank. Do not use any letter more than once.*

_____   1. She's opening the folder.

_____   2. She's opening the drawer.

_____   3. She's flipping through files.

_____   4. She's sticking a label on.

_____   5. The files are alphabetically arranged.

_____   6. The files are color-coded.

a.

b.

c.

d.

e.

f.

B. **Filling in**. *Fill in each blank with the best word from the list.*

about   larger   on   through

1. You can stick a label _____ the tab of a file folder.

2. You flip _____ files to find the one you want.

3. You file information _____ your customers.

4. A legal-size folder is _____ than a letter-size folder.

C. **Listening**. *Listen to the recording and circle the best word or phrase to complete each statement.*

1. file it / set up a new one / put a label on it

2. arranged them alphabetically / opened them / color-coded them

3. filed it / re-filed it / arranged it

4. a folder / a drawer / a filing cabinet

A. *Cross out the one item in parentheses ( ) that doesn't fit well with the underlined verb. The first one is done for you as an example.*

1. You can <u>close</u> (a lid, ~~a sheet~~, a panel, the rings of a binder).

2. You can <u>align</u> (a document on the glass of a copier, a repair service, pages in a paper punch).

3. You can <u>remove</u> (the display of a copier, a staple that went in wrong, a piece of jammed paper, your original from the glass of a copier).

4. You can <u>put</u> (papers in a folder, one sheet on top of another, a sign on a machine, the settings darker).

5. You can <u>make</u> (copies, holes in something, one sheet on top of another).

B. *Fill in each blank with the best word from the list to complete each description. Do not use any word more than once.*

entering	laying	licking	pressing	putting	stacking	turning

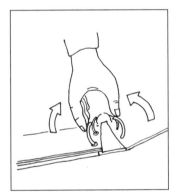 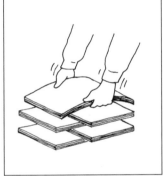  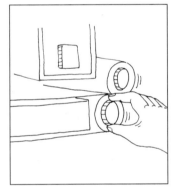

1. She's _____ the rings together.

2. He's _____ the sets crosswise.

3. She's _____ the number of copies she wants.

4. She's _____ a knob.

 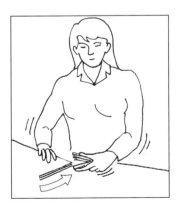 

5. He's _____ his thumb and forefinger.

6. She's _____ a set of papers into a stapler.

7. He's _____ out the papers in order.

C. *Match each item in Column A with the best meaning or description from Column B.*
   Write the letter in the blank.

	Column A		Column B
_____	1. a jam	a.	a folder and the papers inside it
_____	2. to arrange	b.	to make your special instructions (to a machine) go away
_____	3. a document	c.	the edge of a closed book or folder
_____	4. to run out of something	d.	to have no more of something
_____	5. extras	e.	something that is stuck inside a machine
_____	6. a file	f.	to use your fingers to move papers or files very quickly
_____	7. to flip through	g.	with its front side down
_____	8. a spine	h.	to put in order, according to a pattern
_____	9. to clear settings	i.	more than you need
_____	10. face-down	j.	a written thing

D. *Listen to the tape/CD and circle the item which best completes the statement.*

1. a file / a stapler / a full set
2. putting the pages in order / stapling the pages / aligning the pages
3. corner-stapling the papers / clipping the pages together / slipping the pages onto the rings
4. cleaning the glass / clearing the settings / enlarging the copies
5. side-stapling something / stapling a set again / reloading a stapler
6. is jammed / doesn't work / has run out of paper

25. Receiving and Distributing Mail

A. **Matching**. *Match each picture with its description. Write the letter in the blank. Do not use any letter more than once.*

a. removing mail from a mailbox

b. sliding mail into a mailbox

c. opening an envelope

d. stamping the date received on mail

e. sorting mail

f. delivering mail

 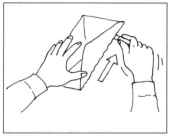

1. _____   2. _____

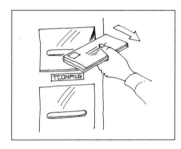  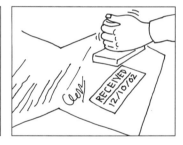 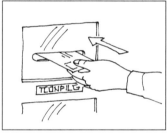

3. _____   4. _____   5. _____   6. _____

B. **Filling in**. *Fill in each blank with the best word or phrase from the list given. Do not use any item more than once.*

| An enclosure | Incoming mail | Junk mail |
| Confidential mail | Interoffice mail | Outgoing mail |

1. _____ is something extra that is included with a letter or memo.

2. _____ is unwanted mail, often advertising.

3. _____ is meant to be private.

4. _____ is to be delivered outside the company.

5. _____ is delivered to a company.

6. _____ is delivered to different offices or departments within the same company.

C. **Listening**. *Listen to the tape/CD and circle the best word or phrase to complete each statement.*

1. tossed it / unfolded it / folded it

2. outgoing mail / recycle bin / mail cart

3. folded it / tossed it / unfolded it

4. wrapper / paper clip / date

5. mail cart / mailbox / mail slot

6. incoming mail / outgoing mail

26. Preparing Items to be Mailed

A. *Filling in.* Fill in each blank with the best word or phrase from the list. Do not use any item more than once.

adding   addressing   correcting   proofreading   putting   sealing   stapling   typing

1. Matt is _____ an envelope.

2. Matt is _____ the draft for errors.

3. Tina is _____ the envelope.

4. Tina is _____ a return-address label.

5. Matt is _____ an error.

6. Tina is _____ an attachment to the letter.

7. Matt is _____ a letter.

8. Tina is _____ the letter and attachment into the envelope.

B. *For each list, cross out the item that does not fit the description.*

1. Parts of a letter: date, salutation, draft, address, body
2. Things that go inside an envelope: letter, attachment, address label, enclosure
3. Packing materials: bubble wrap, shredded paper, styrofoam peanuts, attachments
4. Steps in packing a box: wrapping item, proofreading, packing box, taping box, labeling box

C. *Listening. Listen to the tape/CD. What does the word "it" refer to in each statement? Circle the answer.*

1. enclosure / attachment / envelope
2. the draft / his computer / the flap
3. the letter / the envelope / the label
4. the enclosure / the error / the label
5. the package / the equipment / the error
6. the package / the letter / the label

27. Putting on Postage/Sending out Mail

A. **Filling in**. *Fill in each blank with the best word or phrase from the list.*
Do not use any item more than once.

| amount | display | moistened | postage meter | postage scale |

1. Albert _____ a stamp for the envelope.
2. Tina put a parcel on the _____ .
3. Albert found the _____ of postage needed on the postage rate chart.
4. The _____ stamped the correct amount of postage on the envelope.
5. The scale's _____ showed how much postage to use.

B. **Matching**. *Match each picture with its description. Write the letter in the blank.*
Do not use any item more than once.

_____ 1. The postage meter is printing a sticky label.

_____ 2. Tina is applying the postage label to the package.

_____ 3. Albert is tearing stamps out of a stamp booklet.

_____ 4. Albert is weighing a piece of mail.

_____ 5. Tina slid her envelope through the slot in the postage meter.

_____ 6. Tina pushed the buttons on the postage meter.

a

b

c

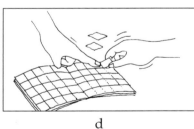
d

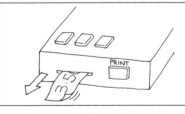
e

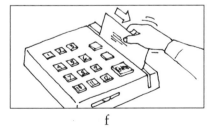
f

C. **Listening**. *Listen to the tape/CD and circle the word or phrase that is part of what the speaker says.*

1. parcel / package / postage
2. sticky / thick / postage
3. label / rate / meter
4. button / basket / booklet
5. chart / display / parcel
6. mail room / postage scale / mail clerk

28. Using an Express Delivery Service

A. **Matching**. *Match each word or phrase with the best definition or description. Write the letter in the blank. Do not use any letter more than once.*

_____ 1. waybill	a. going quickly
_____ 2. status	b. business
_____ 3. receipt	c. form used for express delivery
_____ 4. express	d. condition
_____ 5. pick up	e. statement showing payment made
_____ 6. service	f. go and get something

B. **Filling in**. *Fill in each blank with the best word or phrase from the list. Do not use any item more than once.*

bringing   checking   filling out   giving   measuring   putting   sealing   sticking

1. Matt is _____ files in a box.

2. He is _____ the box.

3. He is _____ the box.

4. He is _____ the waybill.

5. Matt is _____ the waybill to the box.

6. Alice is _____ a package to the delivery service office.

7. She is _____ the price chart.

8. The clerk is _____ Alice a copy of the waybill.

C. **Listening**. *Listen to the tape/CD. Circle the description of the activity each speaker is involved in.*

1. calling a delivery service / dropping off a package

2. measuring a package / weighing a package

3. checking the status of a package / filling out a waybill

4. sealing a box / adding packing material / gathering files

5. weighing a package / checking delivery prices / measuring a package

29. Receiving an Express Package

A. **Matching**. *Match each picture with its description. Write the letter in the blank. Do not use any letter more than once.*

a. removing the contents
b. signing for a package
c. seeing that something is missing
d. reporting a problem
e. receiving a package
f. filling out a form

1. _____   2. _____

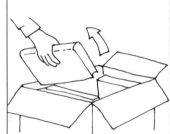

3. _____   4. _____   5. _____   6. _____

B. **Filling in**. *Fill in each blank with the best word or phrase from the list. Do not use any word more than once.*

claim form   damaged   fill out   late   lost   make sure   trace   tracking number

1. If something is broken, you may also say it is _____ .

2. If there is a problem with your delivery, you may _____ a _____ .

3. If your package is _____ the delivery company will _____ it.

4. A package that arrives after it was supposed to is _____ .

5. To trace a package, it is helpful to have your _____ .

6. When a package arrives, you _____ nothing is missing or damaged.

C. **Listening**. *Listen to the tape/CD and circle the best word or phrase to complete each statement.*

1. claim form / delivery person / contents

2. signed for it / traced it / sent it

3. report it / open it / sign for it

4. new / damaged / sent

A. *Cross out the one item in the parentheses ( ) that does not fit well with the underlined verb.*
The first one is done for you as an example.

1. People can <u>receive</u> (a package, junk mail, ~~an outgoing basket,~~ a receipt).
2. People can <u>seal</u> (an envelope, a stamp, a box, a package).
3. People can <u>remove</u> (the contents of a box, letters from envelopes, mail from slots,
   postage from rate charts).
4. People can <u>add</u> (a slot to a postage meter, a label to a parcel, packing material to a box,
   an enclosure to an envelope).
5. People can <u>check</u> (a mailbox, a chart, the status of a package, a delivery person).
6. People can <u>open</u> (stamps, envelopes, boxes, parcels).
7. People can <u>put</u> (mail on the postage scale, a postage label on the scale, stamps on an envelope,
   enclosures into an envelope).

B. *Fill in each blank with the best word from the list to complete each description.*
Do not use any item more than once.

addressing   attaching   folding   handing   signing for   sorting   stamping   weighing

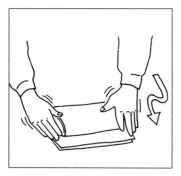

1. He is _____
   a letter.

2. She is _____
   the mail to her
   coworker.

3. He is _____
   the package.

4. She is _____
   the package.

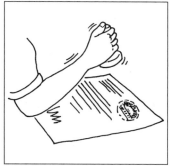

5. He is _____
   the mail.

6. She is _____
   the date on a letter.

7. He is _____
   an envelope.

8. She is _____
   a document to the
   letter.

C. *Match each item in Column A with the best meaning or description from Column B.*
   Write the letter in the blank. Do not use any letter more than once.

Column A	Column B
_____ 1. confidential	a. to cover or place something around an object
_____ 2. contents	b. shows who sent a piece of mail
_____ 3. gather	c. condition or state of something
_____ 4. label	d. secret; to be seen by only certain people
_____ 5. receipt	e. to bring together
_____ 6. return address	f. to put an address on a package
_____ 7. sign	g. item(s) contained in something
_____ 8. status	h. to try to follow and find something
_____ 9. trace	i. to write one's name on a letter or other document
_____ 10. wrap	j. a piece of paper showing that something has been paid for

D. *Listen to the tape/CD and circle the item which best completes the statement.*

1. addressing an envelope / packing a box / opening a package

2. printer / scale / mail cart

3. a lost package / a delivery person / weighing a box

4. signing a letter / proofreading a letter / stamping a letter

5. delivery pickup / delivery waybills / delivery service

6. sorting mail / stamping the date on mail / tossing junk mail in the recycling bin

30. Finding Telephone Numbers

A. **Filling in**. *Fill in each blank with the best word or phrase from the list. Do not use any item more than once.*

dialing   flipping through   giving   looking in   running   searching

1. Alice is _____ the pages of the telephone directory.

2. She is _____ her finger down the list of names in the phone book.

3. Matt is _____ the directory assistance operator.

4. The operator is _____ Matt the number.

5. Alice is _____ the Internet for a phone number.

6. Matt is _____ his rotary file for a number.

B. **Matching**. *Match each word with the best definition or description. Write the letter in the blank. Do not use any letter more than once.*

_____ 1. area code   a. a directory containing phone numbers for people and businesses

_____ 2. listing   b. calls inside a certain area

_____ 3. local calls   c. the first part of a phone number which indicates a certain area

_____ 4. long distance calls   d. the name of a person or business in the phone book

_____ 5. white pages   e. a directory containing advertisements for businesses and services

_____ 6. yellow pages   f. calls going to a number outside your calling area

C. **Listening**. *Listen to the tape/CD and circle the word or phrase that is part of what the speaker says.*

1. took out / wrote down / looked up

2. listing / listening / distance

3. directory / listing / Internet

4. dial / find / file

5. directory assistance / long distance / telephone directory

31. Answering a Telephone Call

A. **Matching**. *Match each word with the best definition or description. Write the letter in the blank.*
Do not use any letter more than once.

_____	1. end	a.	part of telephone held next to ear and mouth
_____	2. flash	b.	go on and off quickly
_____	3. identify	c.	allows one phone to receive and make more than one call at a time
_____	4. phone line	d.	finish
_____	5. reason	e.	say who or what you are
_____	6. receiver	f.	cause

B. **Filling in**. *Fill in each blank with the best word or phrase from the list. Do not use any item more than once.*

flashed   identified   pushed   reason   said goodbye   said hello

1. When Matt answered the phone, he _____ himself.
2. Tina picked up the phone and _____ .
3. When Matt's phone rang, one of the phone line buttons _____ .
4. He _____ the button and answered the phone.
5. Tina gave her _____ for calling Matt.
6. When their conversation ended, the people _____ to each other.

C. **Listening**. *Listen to the tape/CD. Write the number of each description below the picture that best matches it.*

a. _____

b. _____

c. _____

d. _____

e. _____

f. _____

32. Making a Telephone Call

A. **Filling in**. *Fill in each blank with the best word or phrase from the list.*
Do not use the same word more than once.

dial tone   directory   explain   open   secretary

1. A _____ is the sound a caller hears when the phone is ready for use.

2. A telephone book can also be called a _____ .

3. When a phone line isn't being used, it is _____ .

4. A _____ is an assistant to someone who works in a company.

5. When you _____ something, you give the reason for it.

B. **Matching**. *Match each picture with its description. Write the letter in the blank.*
Do not use any letter more than once.

a. looking up a phone number
b. pushing down a button for an open phone line
c. dialing a number
d. identifying oneself
e. explaining why he is calling
f. asking to speak to someone

1. _____

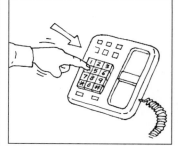

2. _____

3. _____

4. _____

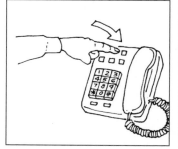

5. _____

6. _____

C. **Listening**. *Listen to the tape/CD. Circle the description of the activity each speaker is involved in.*

1. identifying oneself / asking to speak to someone / answering the phone

2. picking up the receiver / listening as the phone rings / dialing a phone number

3. a secretary answering the phone / a secretary identifying herself / a caller explaining why he called

4. looking up a phone number / answering the phone / identifying oneself

5. a secretary answering the phone / a secretary identifying herself / a caller explaining why he called

6. a secretary answering the phone / a caller identifying himself / a caller explaining why he called

33. Transferring Calls

A. *Filling in.* Fill in each blank with the best word or phrase from the list.

announcing   dialing   hanging up   looking up   pushing   putting

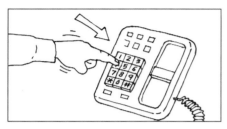

1. Tina is _____ Matt's extension.

Will you hold please?

2. She is _____ the caller on hold.

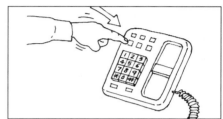

3. She is _____ the transfer button.

DIRECTORY
JOHNSON, M 7895
SMITH, A 1613
TURNER, B 3604
WILSON, K 2016
YEATS, J 1615

4. Tina is _____ Matt's extension in the company directory.

Matt, your call....

5. She is _____ the call to Matt.

6. She is _____ the phone.

B. **Matching**. Match each word with the best definition or description. Write the letter in the blank. Do not use any letter more than once.

_____	1. announce a call	a.	a person's phone number within a company
_____	2. company directory	b.	waiting
_____	3. disconnected call	c.	move a call from one phone to another
_____	4. extension	d.	call that is cut off or ended before it is complete
_____	5. on hold	e.	tell someone they have a phone call
_____	6. transfer a call	f.	listing of names and phone numbers within a company

C. **Listening**. Listen to the tape/CD and circle the best word or phrase to complete each statement.

1. in the directory / on hold / on the phone

2. extension / hold button / directory

3. in the directory / on hold / with the transfer button

4. hung up / began speaking / pushed the transfer button

5. the call / the extension / the hold button

6. dialing the extension / pushing the button / announcing the call

34. Taking a Message

A. **Matching**. *Match each picture with its description. Write the letter in the blank. Do not use any letter more than once.*

a. answering the phone
b. offering to take a message
c. identifying oneself
d. spelling one's name
e. asking for information
f. filling out a phone-message form

1. _____

2. _____

3. _____

4. _____

5. _____

6. _____

B. **Filling in**. *Fill in the blanks to label the fields on the phone message form.*

caller
date and time
for
message
telephone number

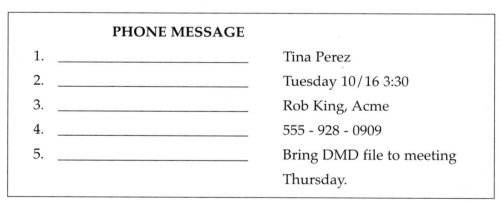

PHONE MESSAGE

1. _____   Tina Perez
2. _____   Tuesday 10/16 3:30
3. _____   Rob King, Acme
4. _____   555 - 928 - 0909
5. _____   Bring DMD file to meeting
                            Thursday.

C. **Listening**. *Listen to the tape/CD. For each statement or question you hear, write the letter of the best response in the blank. Do not use any letter more than once.*

1. _____   a. Hello. May I speak to Matt Johnson, please?
2. _____   b. I'm sorry, she's not available.
3. _____   c. Yes. It's 928-0294.
4. _____   d. Yes, please. This is James Dent from Nebco.
5. _____   e. It's P-E-R-E-Z.

35. Leaving a Message

A. *Filling in*. Fill in each blank with the best word from the list. Do not use any word more than once.

asking   explaining   giving   leave   returns   spelling   telling   thanking

1. Matt is _____ to speak to someone.

2. The secretary is asking Matt to _____ a message.

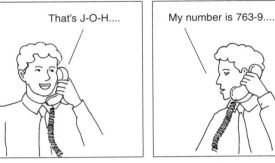

3. Matt is _____ his last name.

4. He is _____ his phone number.

5. He is asking that Ms. Martin _____ his call.

6. He is _____ why he called.

7. He is _____ the secretary when he will be available.

8. He is _____ the secretary.

B. *Matching*. Match the verb on the left with the correct object on the right. Do not use any word more than once.

_____ 1. identify   a. a call
_____ 2. leave   b. a message
_____ 3. return   c. a name
_____ 4. spell   d. yourself

C. *Listening*. Listen to the tape/CD and circle the word or phrase that is part of what the speaker says.

a. secretary / voice mail / answering machine

b. available / voice mail / goodbye

c. identified / explained / thanked

d. name / message / number

36. Sending a Fax

A. *Filling in*. Fill in each blank with the best word or phrase from the list.
   Do not use any word more than once.

   addressee   cover sheet   face down   one by one   scans   sender

   1. When the pages enter the machine _____ , one enters, then another enters.
   2. If a document is _____ , the front side is down or turned over.
   3. The person to whom the fax is sent is called the _____ .
   4. The person who sends the fax is called the _____ .
   5. When the fax machine _____ a document, it takes a picture of it.
   6. The _____ shows the addressee and how many pages are included with the fax.

B. *Matching*. Match each picture with its description. Write the letter in the blank.
   Do not use any letter more than once.

   a. dialing the addressee's fax number
   b. feeding into the fax machine
   c. loading pages face down
   d. preparing a cover sheet
   e. removing pages from the tray
   f. scanning pages

1. _____   2. _____

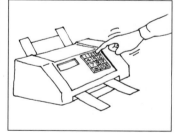

3. _____   4. _____   5. _____   6. _____

C. *Listening*. Listen to the tape/CD and circle the best word or phrase to complete each statement.

   1. face down / ready / send
   2. document / addressee / send button
   3. document return tray / cover sheet / send button
   4. ready / face down / one by one
   5. tray / document / addressee
   6. send / scan / one by one

37. Receiving a Fax

A. **Matching**. Match each word with the best definition or description. Write the letter in the blank. Do not use any letter more than once.

_____	1. beep	a. not in the correct place; lost
_____	2. illegible	b. person who receives something
_____	3. incoming	c. arriving
_____	4. missing	d. leaving
_____	5. outgoing	e. difficult to read or unreadable
_____	6. recipient	f. make a high pitched noise

B. **Filling in**. Fill in each blank with the best word or phrase from the list. Do not use the same word more than once.

checked   display   entered   missing   recipient   stapled

1. The _____ on the fax machine showed "receiving".

2. After the machine beeped, pages _____ the paper receive tray.

3. Albert removed the document from the tray and _____ for illegible pages.

4. Albert saw that one page was not there. It was _____ .

5. Albert _____ the pages of the document together.

6. He delivered the fax to its _____ .

C. **Listening**. Listen to the tape/CD. Write the number of each description below the picture that best matches it.

a. _____   b. _____   c. _____

d. _____   e. _____   f. _____

45

38. Dealing with Fax Machine Problems

A. *Filling in*. Fill in each blank with the best word or phrase from the list. Do not use any item more than once.

calling	jammed	looking at	opening	replacing	separating

1. The paper is _____ .

2. Alice is _____ the cover of the machine.

3. She is _____ two pages that were stuck.

4. Albert is _____ the ink cartridge.

5. Alice is _____ the user's manual.

6. Albert is _____ a repair service.

B. *Matching*. Match each word with the best definition or description. Write the letter in the blank. Do not use any letter more than once.

_____ 1. cartridge	a. to spread out a stack of papers by releasing them quickly at one end
_____ 2. fan	b. crowded together tightly
_____ 3. jammed	c. a book giving information about how to use something
_____ 4. light	d. not dark
_____ 5. replace	e. a container that may be replaced or refilled
_____ 6. stack	f. to put one thing where another used to be
_____ 7. stuck	g. a pile or group of things, one on top of the other
_____ 8. user's manual	h. not movable

C. *Listening*. Listen to the tape/CD. In each statement, what does the word "it" refer to? Write the letter of the best answer in the blank. Use each letter only once.

1. _____	a. the cover
2. _____	b. the display
3. _____	c. the document feeder
4. _____	d. the ink cartridge
5. _____	e. the paper tray
6. _____	f. the user's manual

A. Fill in each blank with the best word or phrase from the list to complete each description.
Do not use any item more than once.

dialing   flipping   hanging up   loading   looking up   refilling   removing   spelling   writing down

1. She is _____ through the pages of the phone book.

2. He is _____ the phone.

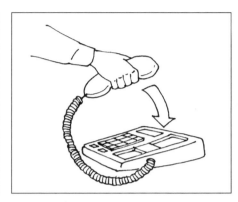

3. She is _____ the phone.

4. She is _____ a number in her rotary file.

That's B-R-A-D....

5. She is _____ her name.

6. He is _____ documents in the feeder.

7. She is _____ documents from the tray.

8. He is _____ the paper tray.

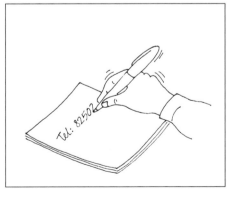

Tel: 82502

9. She is _____ a phone number.

B. For each list, cross out the one item that does not fit the description. The first one is done for you as an example.

1. Parts of a phone: receiver, phone line button, ~~rotary file~~, transfer button
2. Places to find phone numbers: the Internet, an address book, directory assistance, an area code
3. Buttons you press: hold, transfer, send, print, problem
4. Information on a fax cover sheet: date, fax numbers, fax tone, number of pages
5. Fax machine problems: paper jam, receiving, empty paper tray, no ink
6. Parts of a fax machine: document, display, feeder, ink cartridge

C. Match each item in Column A with the best meaning or description from Column B.
Write the letter in the blank. Do not use any letter more than once.

Column A		Column B
_____ 1. addressee		a. cut off before completed
_____ 2. announce		b. unreadable
_____ 3. disconnected		c. name of a person or business in the phone book
_____ 4. extension		d. waiting for someone or something on the phone
_____ 5. fan		e. to make something known; to say aloud
_____ 6. feed		f. phone line within a company or business
_____ 7. illegible		g. person to whom something is sent
_____ 8. listing		h. to spread out
_____ 9. on hold		i. to put into
_____ 10. separate		j. to cause to be apart

D. Listen to the tape/CD and circle the item which best completes the statement.

1. dialing a number / looking up a number / identifying herself
2. leaving a message / taking a message / calling directory assistance
3. putting someone on hold / explaining why she called / transferring a call
4. answering the phone / leaving a message / identifying herself
5. preparing a cover sheet / dialing a fax number / receiving a fax
6. refill the paper tray / replace the ink cartridge / remove a document

39. Starting a Computer

A. *Matching.* Match each picture with its description. Write the letter in the blank.
   Do not use any letter more than once.

a. clicking on an icon
b. a flashing cursor
c. hitting the "on" button on a power strip
d. moving the pointer with the mouse
e. pressing the on/off button on the computer
f. turning on the monitor

1. _____   2. _____

  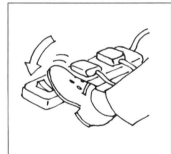 

3. _____   4. _____   5. _____   6. _____

B. *For each list, cross out the one item that does not fit the description.*

1. things you turn on: computer / monitor / power strip / icon

2. parts of a computer: mouse / monitor / mouse pad / CD-Rom drive

3. things a mouse does: points / flashes / clicks / moves

4. things you see on the monitor screen: icon / button / cursor / pointer

C. *Listening.* Listen to the tape/CD and circle the best word or phrase to complete each statement.

1. monitor / power strip / CPU
2. clicking / opening / flashing
3. mouse / program / screen

4. mouse / monitor / icon
5. an icon / the pointer / the mouse
6. monitor / program / screen

40. Shutting Down a Computer

A. **Matching**. *Match each word with the best definition or description. Write the letter in the blank. Do not use any letter more than once.*

_____ 1. choose   a. choice

_____ 2. menu   b. to pick; select

_____ 3. option   c. to turn off

_____ 4. prompt   d. something that asks for information

_____ 5. shut down   e. list of choices

B. **Filling in**. *Fill in each blank with the best word or phrase from the list. Do not use any item more than once.*

asking   choosing   closing   saving   shut down   turned off

1. Albert is _____ the document.

2. He is _____ the program.

3. He is _____ the "shut down" option from the menu.

4. The prompt is _____ Albert if he wants to shut down.

5. The computer has _____ .

6. The monitor has been _____ .

C. **Listening**. *Listen to the tape/CD. In each statement, what does the word "it" refer to? Write the letter of the best answer in the blank. Use each letter only once.*

1. _____   a. the computer

2. _____   b. the document

3. _____   c. the monitor

4. _____   d. the prompt

5. _____   e. the power strip

6. _____   f. the shut-down option

41. Keying in Text

A. **Filling in**. *Fill in each blank with the best word from the list. Do not use any word more than once.*

boldface   capital   delete   enter   indent   shift   space   tab

1. When you _____ a line, you begin it further to the right than usual.
2. A _____ letter is also called an upper-case letter.
3. The _____ key can be used to indent a line.
4. _____ type is darker than normal type.
5. When you _____ between words, you make more room.
6. You can make a new line by hitting the _____ key.
7. If you _____ something, you remove or erase it.
8. To make a capital letter, you can use the _____ key.

B. **Matching**. *Match each picture with its description. Write the letter in the blank.*
Do not use any letter more than once.

a. beginning a new line
b. checking spelling
c. hitting the space bar
d. indenting with the tab key
e. naming a report
f. opening the word-processing program
g. typing a report

1. _____

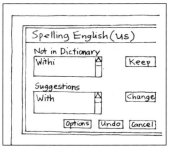

2. _____

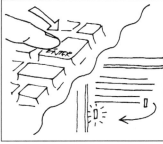

3. _____

4. _____

5. _____

6. _____

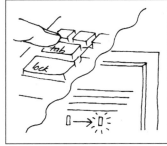

7. _____

C. **Listening**. *Listen to each statement and circle the word or phrase that is part of what the speaker says.*

1. enter / capital letter / shift
2. report / keyboard / tab key
3. opened / pressed / named
4. named / made / saved
5. text / tab / thumb
6. text / spelling / report

51

42. Printing

A. **Filling in**. *Fill in each blank with the best word or phrase from the list given.*
Do not use any word more than once.

feeder　　output tray　　paper guides　　power light　　preview　　set up

1. When you _____ something, you are getting it ready.

2. The document _____ pulls the paper into the printer.

3. When you _____ a document, you see what it will look like when it's printed.

4. The _____ shows whether the printer is on or off.

5. The _____ make sure the paper is straight as it enters the printer.

6. The printed document goes into the _____ .

B. **Matching**. *For each statement below, determine what does the word "it" refer to?*
Write the letter in the blank. Do not use any letter more than once.

_____	1. Tina turned it on.	a. the copy
_____	2. Albert clicked on it to print.	b. the feeder
_____	3. Albert finished it and then he saved it.	c. "OK"
_____	4. Tina removed it from the output tray.	d. the print job
_____	5. Tina set it up.	e. the printer
_____	6. Albert added paper to it.	f. the report

C. **Listening**. *Listen to the tape/CD. Write the number of each description below the picture that best matches it.*

a. _____

b. _____

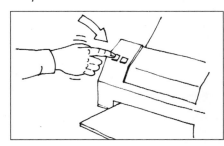

c. _____

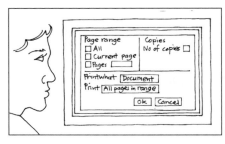

d. _____

e. _____

f. _____

43. Receiving E-mail

A. **Filling in**. *Fill in each blank with the best word from the list below. Do not use any item more than once.*

closing   deleting   double-clicking   entering   exiting   opening   replying   saving

1. Tina is _____ her e-mail account to check her messages.

2. She is _____ her password.

3. Matt is _____ junk mail.

4. He is _____ on a message to open it.

5. Tina is _____ a message.

6. Matt is _____ a message.

7. He is _____ to the sender.

8. Tina is _____ her e-mail program.

B. **Matching**. *Match each word with the best definition or description. Write the letter in the blank. Do not use any letter more than once.*

_____ 1. attachment   a. to write a group of items, one after the other

_____ 2. download   b. a secret word or expression needed to open an e-mail account

_____ 3. forward   c. a document sent along with an e-mail message

_____ 4. junk mail   d. unwanted mail, often advertisements

_____ 5. list   e. to send a message you have received on to someone else

_____ 6. password   f. to copy material from the Internet on to your computer

C. **Listening**. *Listen to the tape/CD and circle the word or phrase that best completes each statement.*

1. attachment / recipient / inbox

2. her account / an attachment / junk mail

3. password / inbox / account

4. recipient / supervisor / sender

5. closed it / double-clicked on it / forwarded it

6. checked her e-mail / exited her e-mail program / opened her e-mail program

44. Sending E-mail

A. ***Matching***. *Match each word with the best definition or description. Write the letter in the blank. Do not use any letter more than once.*

_____	1. e-mail address book
_____	2. attach
_____	3. copy list
_____	4. field
_____	5. recipient
_____	6. scroll through

a. a person who receives something

b. to include something along with an e-mail message

c. to make the information on the screen move up, down, or sideways

d. contains the Internet addresses of people to whom you often send messages

e. a person or group of people receiving a copy of a message you send to someone else

f. on a computer screen, an open space where you can type something

B. *Put the sentences in the correct order to send an e-mail message.*
Write the number "1" for the first step, "2" for the second step, and so on.

_____ a. A new message window opens.

_____ b. She writes the message in the message window.

_____ c. Alice clicks on the "new message" icon.

_____ d. When she is done, she sends the message.

C. ***Listening***. *Listen to the tape/CD. Write the number of each description below the picture that best matches it.*

a. _____

b. _____

c. _____

d. _____

e. _____

f. _____

54

45. Getting Information from the Internet

A. **Matching**. *Match each word with the best definition or description. Write the letter in the blank.
Do not use any letter more than once.*

_____ 1. a book mark
_____ 2. an icon
_____ 3. a URL
_____ 4. a hit
_____ 5. scrolling
_____ 6. clicking

a. moving up or down through a Web page
b. a Web "address"
c. a site that contains what you searched for
d. using a mouse to choose something
e. a small symbol or picture representing a computer program
f. an item in a list of Web sites you visit often

B. *Look at each picture and complete the statement with one of the items from the list.*

link   listed   pointer   typing

1. The _____ is pointing to the scroll bar.

2. The search engine _____ some hits.

3. I'm _____ in a URL.

4. The pointer is clicking on a _____ .

C. **Listening**. *Listen to the tape/CD. In each statement, what does the word "this" refer to? Circle the answer.*

1. a keyword / a link / a URL

2. went on line / went off line / scrolled through

3. clicked on it / typed it in / followed it

4. came up / followed it / listed it

46. Using a Typewriter

A. ***Matching***. *Match each picture with its description. Write the letter in the blank.*
Do not use any letter more than once.

a. addressing an envelope
b. centering the paper
c. completing a form
d. correcting an error
e. feeding the paper into the typewriter

f. pulling the paper out
g. straightening the paper
h. turning the platen knob
i. typing a title

1. _____

2. _____

3. _____

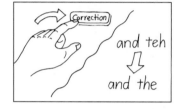

4. _____

5. _____

6. _____

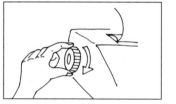

7. _____

8. _____

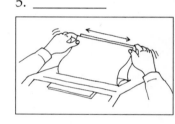

9. _____

B. *For each list, cross out the one item that doesn't fit the description.*

1. parts of a typewriter: platen / keys / paper / paper release lever

2. keys on a typewriter: return / platen / shift / letter / backspace

3. what people use a typewriter for: securing the paper / addressing an envelope / typing labels / completing a form

4. things you do while typing: backspace / correct errors / begin a new line / straighten the keys

C. ***Listening***. *Listen to the tape/CD. In each statement, what does the word "it" refer to?*
Write the letter of the best answer in the blank. Use each letter only once.

1. _____
2. _____
3. _____
4. _____
5. _____
6. _____

a. the margin
b. the platen
c. the platen knob
d. the return key
e. the shift key
f. the typewriter

47. Using a Calculator

A. **Filling in**. *Fill in each blank with the best word from the list. Do not use any word more than once.*

adding   clearing   entering   feeding   printing   subtracting   tearing   totaling

1. Alice is _____ amounts on the keypad.

2. She is _____ the paper up.

3. She is _____ the numbers together.

4. She is _____ an error.

5. The numbers are _____ on the tape.

6. Alice is _____ the final result.

7. She is _____ off the printout.

8. She is _____ the display.

B. *Match each part of a calculator with the best description. Write the letter in the blank.*

_____ 1. display	a. used for subtracting numbers
_____ 2. division key	b. where numbers are printed out
_____ 3. keypad	c. pushed to give the complete amount or final result
_____ 4. minus key	d. used for multiplying numbers
_____ 5. multiplication key	e. window showing last number entered or calculated
_____ 6. paper roll	f. used to add numbers
_____ 7. plus key	g. used to divide numbers
_____ 8. total key	h. face of calculator, where keys are located

C. **Listening**. *Listen to the tape/CD and circle the word or phrase that best completes each statement.*

1. keypad / amount / printout
2. plus key / minus key / total key
3. keypad / display / file
4. subtracted it / printed it / divided it
5. receipt / keypad / printout
6. roll / results / errors

A. *Fill in each blank with the best word or phrase from the list to complete each description. Do not use any item more than once.*

clearing	closing	printing	scrolling	subtracting	turning off
clicking on	moving	pulling	straightening	turning	typing

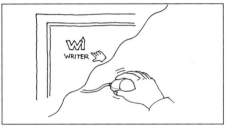

1. She is _____ an icon.

2. He is _____ .

3. She is _____ the calculator.

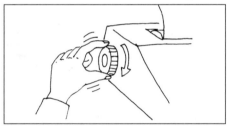

4. He is _____ the platen knob.

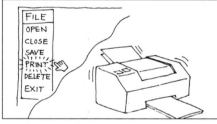

5. Someone is _____ a document.

6. He is _____ through the names in his address book.

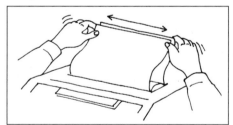

7. She is _____ the paper.

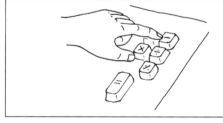

8. Someone is _____ numbers.

9. She is _____ a program.

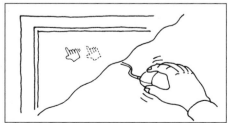

10. He is _____ the pointer.

11. He is _____ the paper out of the typewriter.

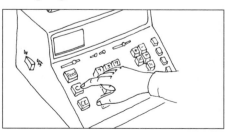

12. Someone is _____ the display.

58

B. Cross out the one item in parentheses ( ) that does not fit well with the underlined verb. The first one is done for you as an example.

1. People can <u>open</u> (a program, ~~a recipient's name,~~ an e-mail message, an e-mail address book).
2. People can <u>click on</u> (icons, "OK," a bookmark, a password).
3. People can <u>turn on</u> (a PC, a power strip, a mouse, a typewriter, a monitor).
4. People can <u>hit</u> (the space bar, the on/off button, the printer, the tab key).
5. People can <u>enter</u> (a password, an enter key, amounts from receipts, numbers).
6. People can <u>type</u> (a label, an upper case letter, a keyword, a printer, a subject line).

C. Match each item in Column A with the best meaning or description from Column B. Write the letter in the blank. Do not use any letter more than once.

Column A		Column B	
_____	1. complete	a.	to connect to the Internet
_____	2. cursor	b.	to answer
_____	3. display	c.	to fill out
_____	4. download	d.	to add numbers together to reach an amount
_____	5. field	e.	blinking line on screen showing where type will appear
_____	6. go on line	f.	small window on calculator where numbers appear
_____	7. keyword	g.	to copy information from the Internet to your computer
_____	8. reply	h.	to turn off
_____	9. shut off	i.	word that is part of a phrase you want to find
_____	10. total	j.	an area in which to type or write information

D. **Listening**. Listen to the tape/CD and circle the item that best completes each statement.

1. using a word processing program / turning on her computer / printing a document
2. deleting junk mail / checking the spelling / attaching a file
3. type a document / delete a document / print a document
4. forward a message / delete a message / reply to a message
5. printer / typewriter / monitor
6. checking her work / entering numbers / clearing the display

48. Receiving an Invoice/Paying

A. **Filling in**. Fill in each blank with the best word or phrase from the list. Do not use any word more than once.

confirm	invoice	make sure	record
detail	issue a check	order	

1. When you _____ information, you write it down.
2. A(n) _____ is a bill; it tells how much should be paid.
3. _____ and _____ are similar. They both mean "to make certain of something".
4. A(n) _____ is a fact or small piece of information.
5. When you _____ , you prepare it so that you may pay for something.
6. When you _____ something, you request it from the seller.

B. **Matching**. Match each picture with its description. Write the letter in the blank. Do not use any letter more than once.

a. issuing a check
b. pulling out an invoice
c. recording payment details
d. separating copies of the invoice
e. signing a check
f. stamping "paid" on the customer's copy

1. _____
2. _____
3. _____

4. _____
5. _____
6. _____

C. **Listening**. Listen to the tape/CD. In each statement, what does the word "it" refer to? Write the letter of the best answer in the blank. Use each letter only once.

1. _____   4. _____
2. _____   5. _____
3. _____   6. _____

a. the check
b. the customer copy of the invoice
c. the invoice
d. the package
e. the purchase order
f. the vendor's copy of the invoice

49. Issuing a Check

A. **Filling in**. *Fill in each blank with the best word or phrase from the list. Do not use any item more than once.*

clicking on   opening   payee   printed   signing   stub   tearing out   writing out

1. Tina is _____ a check for computer equipment.

2. She is filling out the check _____ .

3. She is _____ the check.

4. She is _____ the check.

5. Albert is _____ his check-writing software.

6. He is entering the _____ in the open fields.

7. He is _____ the print command.

8. The check is being _____ .

B. **Matching**. *Match each word with the best definition or description. Write the letter in the blank. Do not use any letter more than once.*

_____ 1. account number

_____ 2. amount

_____ 3. check stub

_____ 4. field

_____ 5. numeral

_____ 6. payee

a. person or company who is to receive the check

b. quantity; value of check

c. number

d. identification number used by bank

e. area where information is entered or written

f. remains in check folder or book to leave a record of the check

C. **Listening**. *Listen to the tape/CD. Write the date, payee, and amount in the blanks of each check below. Write the information in the open fields.*

1.
FIRST SAVINGS. DENSTAR CORP

Date _____

Payee _____

Amount _____

$ _____

9282 1003216

2.
FIRST SAVINGS. DENSTAR CORP

Date _____

Payee _____

Amount _____

$ _____

50. Sending Out a Bill

A. **Filling in.** *Fill in each blank with the best word or phrase from the list.*
Do not use the same word more than once.

bill   customer   double-check   due   overdue   prepare

1. When you _____ something, you check or review it again.

2. A _____ is a piece of paper that tells how much you have to pay.

3. If a payment is _____ , now is the time to pay.

4. When you _____ something, you get it ready.

5. A _____ is a person or company who buys something.

6. If a payment is _____ , it is late.

B. **Matching.** *Match each picture with its description. Write the letter in the blank.*
Do not use any letter more than once.

a. double-checking the amount due
b. filing a copy of the invoice
c. preparing an invoice for a customer

d. printing an invoice
e. reviewing the purchase order
f. sending the invoice to the customer

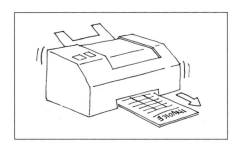

1. _____

2. _____

3. _____

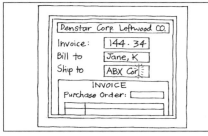

4. _____

5. _____

6. _____

C. **Listening.** *Listen to the tape/CD and circle the best word or phrase to complete each statement.*

1. bill / price / customer

2. purchase order / amount / file

3. total / bill / due

4. invoice / price / copy

5. file / item / total

6. copy / customer / purchase order

51. Receiving Payment

A. **Matching**. *Match each word with the best definition or description. Write the letter in the blank.*
Do not use any letter more than once.

_____ 1. accounts receivable file
_____ 2. endorse
_____ 3. endorsement
_____ 4. payment
_____ 5. post
_____ 6. safe

a. to sign or stamp your name on the back of a check
b. a name placed on the back of a check
c. to record; make a written note of
d. a listing of payments to be made to your company
e. strong, thick-sided box with a lock used to hold valuable objects
f. the act of giving money that is owed

B. **Filling in**. *Fill in each blank with the best word or phrase from the list. Do not use any word more than once.*

endorsing   filing   placing   posting   recording   stamping

1. Matt is _____ a payment date in the accounts receivable file.

2. He is _____ a check.

3. He is _____ the payment in the computer file.

4. Matt is _____ the invoice as paid.

5. He is _____ the check in the safe.

6. He is _____ the invoice.

C. **Listening**. *Listen to the tape/CD. In each statement, what does the word "this" refer to? Circle the answer.*

1. accounts receivable file / safe
2. endorsed it / filed it
3. payment / paid
4. the invoice / the payment
5. the information / the safe
6. the computer / the invoice

52. Working with Petty Cash

A. **Matching**. *Match each word with the best definition or description. Write the letter in the blank.*
   Do not use any letter more than once.

   _____ 1. approve   a. a small amount of money available to pay small expenses

   _____ 2. carbon copy   b. to show you agree

   _____ 3. petty cash   c. a duplicate (copy) made using a special type of paper

   _____ 4. reimbursement d. a kind of receipt given to show money has been paid

   _____ 5. strong box   e. money that is "paid back" to you

   _____ 6. voucher   f. a metal container used to hold valuable things

B. **Filling in**. *Fill in each blank with the best word or phrase from the list.*
   Do not use any letter more than once.

   carbon copy   counted   petty cash   reimbursement   signed   unlocked

   1. Tina brought a receipt for _____ .

   2. Matt filled out a _____ voucher.

   3. Matt _____ the petty cash strongbox.

   4. He _____ out the correct amount of money for Tina.

   5. Tina _____ the voucher.

   6. Matt tore out the voucher, leaving a _____ behind.

C. **Listening**. *Listen to the tape/CD. Write the number of each description below the picture that best matches it.*

a. _____

b. _____

c. _____

d. _____

e. _____

f. _____

A. *Fill in each blank with the best word or phrase from the list to complete each description.*
Do not use any item more than once.

comparing	endorsing	filing	mailing	separating	stamping
counting	entering	filling out	recording	signing	unlocking

1. The man is _____
the purchase order and invoice.

2. She is _____
a check.

3. She is _____
copies of the invoice.

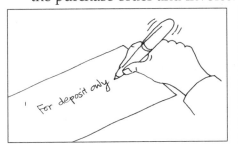

4. He is _____
a check.

5. She is _____
an invoice.

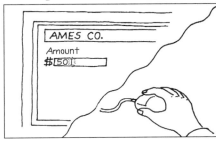

6. He is _____
a payment.

7. She is _____
an invoice.

8. He is _____
information in the fields.

9. She is _____
an invoice.

10. He is _____
a petty cash voucher

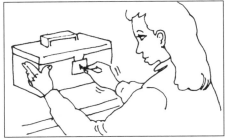

11. She is _____
the petty cash box.

12. He is _____
out money.

B. *For each list, cross out the one item that does not fit the description. The first one is done for you as an example.*

1. Things you do to a check: issue it, ~~open it,~~ sign it, endorse it, tear it out

2. Fields on a check: stamp, payee, date, amount

3. Things you do to an invoice: prepare it, stamp it, file it, send it, tear it

4. Things you fill out: a petty cash voucher, the total amount due, a check, a check stub

5. Things you do to a payment: post it, review it, record it, print it

C. *Match each item in Column A with the best meaning or description from Column B. Write the letter in the blank.*

Column A		Column B
_____ 1. accounts receivable	a.	a receipt given to show money has been paid
_____ 2. approve	b.	to review something again
_____ 3. double-check	c.	a bill
_____ 4. invoice	d.	to record or make a note of
_____ 5. issue	e.	a request to buy something
_____ 6. post	f.	money returned or paid back
_____ 7. prepare	g.	to get ready
_____ 8. purchase order	h.	payments to be made to a company
_____ 9. reimbursement	i.	to agree
_____ 10. voucher	j.	to make or bring out

D. *Listen to the tape/CD and circle the item that best completes each statement.*

1. an invoice / a petty cash voucher / a purchase order

2. approved the voucher / filed the voucher / stamped the voucher

3. tearing out a check / opening his check-writing software / issuing a check

4. post a payment / stamp an invoice / place a check in the safe

5. order something / separate copies of the invoice / compare the purchase order and invoice

53. Getting Supplies from a Stockroom

A. **Filling in**. *Fill in each blank with the best word or phrase from the list.*
Do not use any word more than once.

amount   inventory   note   on hand   requisition   supply room

1. A list of items a company has available for use is called its _____ .

2. A(n) _____ is a request (in writing) for something.

3. _____ means "quantity".

4. When you _____ something, you write it down.

5. Something that is _____ is available and ready to be used.

6. A place where items are kept until needed is called a _____ .

B. **Matching**. *Match each picture with its description. Write the letter in the blank.*
Do not use any letter more than once.

a. crossing out an amount on an inventory sheet
b. filling out a requisition form
c. noting the new amount

d. opening the supply cabinet
e. taking something out of the cabinet
f. unpacking a box

1. _____

2. _____

3. _____

4. _____

5. _____

6. _____

C. **Listening**. *Listen to the tape/CD and circle the word or phrase that is part of what the speaker says.*

1. order / open

2. supply cabinet / stockroom

3. noted / noticed

4. ordered / opened

5. crossed out / filled out

6. noted / noticed

54. Dealing with Accidents

A. *Filling in*. Fill in each blank with the best word or phrase from the list. Do not use any item more than once.

bandaged   completed   cut   emergency number   fell   first aid kit   injured   paramedics

1. Matt _____ on the wet floor.

2. He _____ his leg.

3. Alice called the _____ .

4. The _____ brought Matt to the hospital.

5. Alice _____ an accident report.

6. Tina _____ her finger.

7. She got out the _____ .

8. She cleaned and _____ her wound.

B. *Matching*. Match each statement with the best meaning for "this" or "they" in that statement. Write the letter in the blank. Do not use any letter more than once.

_____ 1. Alice did this when she slipped in the hall.

_____ 2. She injured her back and couldn't do this.

_____ 3. Albert called this.

_____ 4. They brought Alice to the hospital.

_____ 5. Albert got an accident report and did this.

a. completed it
b. emergency number
c. fell
d. move
e. paramedics

C. *Listening*. Listen to the tape/CD and circle the best word or phrase to complete each statement.

1. minor injury / serious injury

2. first aid kit / accident / wound

3. paramedics / first aid kit / emergency number

4. slipped / couldn't move / stayed with Matt

5. minor accident / serious accident

6. break room / hospital / first aid kit

55. Handling Maintenance Problems

A. **Filling in**. *Fill in each blank with the best word or phrase from the list. Do not use any item more than once.*

building maintenance   burned out   changed   mopped up   noticed   problem   replaced   spill

1. Matt saw that the light in his office was _____ .

2. A maintenance worker _____ the bad bulb.

3. Albert discovered a _____ in the breakroom.

4. He called _____ _____ .

5. The janitor came and _____ the spill.

6. Tina _____ that the office was unusually warm.

7. The maintenance person found a _____ with the thermostat.

8. The repair person _____ the thermostat.

B. **Matching**. *In each sentence below, what does "it" refer to? Write the letter of the best meaning in the blank. Use each letter only once.*

_____ 1. It was burned out.

_____ 2. The janitor mopped it.

_____ 3. The plumber fixed it.

_____ 4. The maintenance worker left it near the spill.

_____ 5. She left it for the night maintenance worker.

_____ 6. It was very wet.

_____ 7. There was a problem with it so the office was too warm.

a. air conditioning
b. a broken pipe
c. a carpet
d. a light bulb
e. a note
f. a spill
g. a warning sign

C. **Listening**. *Listen to the tape/CD. For each statement or question you hear, write the letter of the best response in the blank. Do not use the same letter more than once.*

1. _____
2. _____
3. _____
4. _____
5. _____

a. I'll change the bad bulb.
b. Thanks. This feels much better.
c. I'm really warm too.
d. I'll send a janitor to mop it up.
e. I'll send a plumber right away.

56. Handling Office Security

A. **Filling in**. *Fill in each blank with the best word or phrase from the list.*
Do not use any word more than once.

activated   alarm   confidential   escort   mumbles   out of sight   precaution   shred

1. Something that is _____ is secret.

2. A(n) _____ is something that is done to prevent something else from happening.

3. If something is _____ , it is hidden from view.

4. When something has been _____ , it is on or ready.

5. Someone who _____ has not spoken clearly.

6. A(n) _____ is something that gives a warning.

7. When you _____ something, you tear it into small pieces.

8. When you _____ someone, you go with him or her.

B. **Matching**. *Match each picture with its description. Write the letter in the blank.*
Do not use any letter more than once.

a. keeping purses and bags out of sight
b. locking doors and desks
c. punching in the alarm code
d. reporting an unwanted visitor
e. shredding documents
f. using security screens

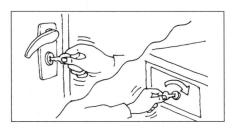

I just saw a suspicious man.

1. _____   2. _____   3. _____

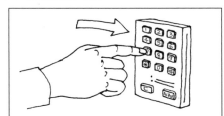

4. _____   5. _____   6. _____

C. **Listening**. *Listen to the recording and circle the best word or phrase to complete each statement.*

1. pages / feeder / paper clips
2. recycle bin / file cabinet / hallway
3. confidential / activated / unfamiliar
4. alarm / screen / hallway
5. out of sight / out of the building
6. out of sight / out of the building

70

A. *Fill in each blank with the best word or phrase from the list to complete each description.*
Do not use any item more than once.

bandaging   calling   crossing out   escorting   fixing   opening   punching   replacing   shredding

1. The woman is _____ the supply cabinet.

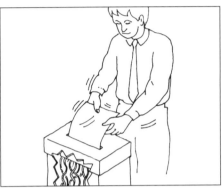

2. The man is _____ documents.

3. The guard is _____ an unwanted visitor out.

4. The maintenance worker is _____ the light bulb.

5. He is _____ a number on the form.

6. She is _____ in the alarm code.

7. He is _____ a broken pipe.

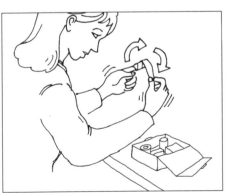

8. She is _____ her finger.

We have an injured person.

9. She is _____ the emergency number.

B. *For each list, cross out the one item that does not fit the description. The first one is done for you as an example.*

1. Things in a stockroom: supply cabinets, inventory sheets, ~~guards~~, boxes
2. Forms you complete: inventory sheets, accident reports, requisitions, reams of paper
3. Maintenance problems: falls, spills, bad light bulbs, broken air conditioning
4. People who handle maintenance problems: janitors, plumbers, repair people, paramedics
5. Security precautions: lock desks, mop up spills, report suspicious visitors, set alarms, shred documents

C. *Match each item in Column A with the best meaning or description from Column B.*
Write the letter in the blank. Do not use any letter more than once.

Column A		**Column B**	
_____	1. alarm	a.	to see
_____	2. deal with	b.	can't be seen
_____	3. get rid of	c.	something that gives a warning
_____	4. inventory	d.	to do something about
_____	5. maintenance	e.	list of goods or items on hand or available
_____	6. notice	f.	to tell about
_____	7. out of sight	g.	to give or throw away
_____	8. precaution	h.	a request to buy something
_____	9. report	i.	something done to keep something else from happening
_____	10. requisition	j.	taking care of something

D. *Listen to the tape/CD and circle the item that best completes the statement.*

1. burned out bulb / broken thermostat / spill
2. getting the first aid kit / completing an accident report / calling an emergency number
3. fill out a requisition form / stack the paper / unpack a box
4. an unwanted visitor / locking desks / shredding documents
5. locked the door / activated the alarm / called security

SECTION I: Daily Routines

1. Getting Ready for Work
Exercise C

NARRATOR:
Number one: Matt put some papers for work in his ....
Number two: Before work, Matt packed a lunch in ....
Number three: Tina wore pants and a polo shirt. She wore ....
Number four: Matt wore a jacket and shirt and tie. He wore ....
Number five: Matt stopped at the dry cleaners to drop off some ....
Number six: When Tina woke up, she took ....

2. Arriving at the Office
Exercise C

NARRATOR:
Number one: She entered the building. She used ....
Number two: She went up to her floor. She used ....
Number three: She unlocked her door. She used ....
Number four: She made some small talk with her ....
Number five: She took some papers out of ....
Number six: She parked her car in ....

3. Going through Security
Exercise C

NARRATOR:
Number one: Good morning.
Number two: Sorry, sir. No one can enter without an ID.
Number three: Next time you'll need an ID.
Number four: You can go in now.
Number five: Do you know this man, Ms Perez?
Number six: Where do you work?

4. Reporting for Work
Exercise C

NARRATOR:
Number one: The board showed that Alice was in.
Number two: Albert went to the time clock and punched in.
Number three: Matt checked the clock to find out the time.
Number four: He put his card back in the rack.
Number five: The time clock printed the date.
Number six: I opened the book to the right page.

Number seven: My marker was in the out column.
Number eight: You should write your name in the book.

5. Getting Settled at the Office
Exercise C

NARRATOR:
Number one: Watering something.
Number two: Setting something on a desk.
Number three: Rolling up his sleeves.
Number four: Arranging something.
Number five: Pouring a drink.
Number six: Hanging something up.
Number seven: Turning something on.
Number eight: Sipping a drink.

6. Planning Your Day/Scheduling
Exercise C

NARRATOR: Number one.
WOMAN: I meet with John at noon, but I'm free after that.

NARRATOR: Number two.
MAN: I'll write the dinner on my calendar, but we might have to change it.

NARRATOR: Number three.
WOMAN: I'm supposed to meet Tina at two, but Mr. Bates just called a two o'clock meeting.

NARRATOR: Number four.
MAN: Sorry. But I have to cancel our ten-thirty. Could we meet at three-fifteen instead?

7. Checking Voicemail Messages
Exercise C

NARRATOR:
Number one: Tina didn't need a voicemail message so she ....
Number two: Matt didn't hear a message so he ....
Number three: Tina had an important voicemail message so she ....
Number four: Matt replayed a message because he ....
Number five: When Matt finished listening to his messages he ....
Number six: As Tina listened to a message, she ....

8. Taking a Coffee Break
Exercise C

NARRATOR:
Number one: Would you like a cookie, Alice?
Number two: Do you think this rain will stop soon?
Number three: Let's see, 25, 50, 75. I've got enough.
Number four: Oh, look, it says here the company picnic is in two weeks.
Number five: Hmm. The chips look good but so do the cookies.
Number six: I'd better get back to my desk. See you later.

9. Eating Lunch in a Cafeteria
Exercise C

NARRATOR:
Number one: Ordering food.
Number two: Ringing up.
Number three: Spooning up.
Number four: Going through line.
Number five: Throwing away.
Number six: Joining coworkers.
Number seven: Taking a tray.
Number eight: Making a salad.

10. Eating a Bag Lunch
Exercise C

NARRATOR:
Number one: Alice took her bag lunch out of the ....
Number two: Albert set the timer on the ....
Number three: Alice poured coffee from her ....
Number four: Matt crumpled up his empty bag and ....
Number five: Alice snapped the cover on her ....
Number six: Tina took the plastic container out and ....

11. Spending Lunchtime in Other Ways
Exercise C

NARRATOR:
Number one: I'd like the special.
Number two: How much will the postage be for this?
Number three: Could I make an appointment for a haircut, please?
Number four: I'd better put this in my savings account.
Number five: I'll be finished working out in 10 minutes.
Number six: Hmm. I think I'll buy this one.

12. Ending the Workday
Exercise C

NARRATOR:
Number one: Alice shut off her computer.
Number two: Albert looked at his to-do list.
Number three: Matt put some papers in his file.

Number four: Alice turned off the lights.
Number five: Matt locked the filing cabinet.

13. Leaving the Office
Exercise C

NARRATOR:
Number one: Matt found his name in the sign-in book.
Number two: She signed out.
Number three: He found his name.
Number four: He checked the time.
Number five: The board showed he was out.
Number six: She found her name on the line.

REVIEW EXERCISES - Section I

Exercise D

NARRATOR: Number one.
MAN: Well, it looks like we'd better get back to work.

NARRATOR: Number two.
WOMAN: I've worked here for a long time.
MAN: Sorry, we can't remember everyone.
NARRATOR: The man does not ....

NARRATOR: Number three.
MAN: Here are some clothes I need dry-cleaned. When will they be ready?
NARRATOR: He is ....

NARRATOR: Number four.
WOMAN: What did you do last weekend?
MAN: Not much. What about you?
NARRATOR: They are ....

NARRATOR: Number five.
MAN: Five, six, seven, eight, nine.
NARRATOR: He is ....

NARRATOR: Number six.
WOMAN: Could I have the fish, please, and some salad?
NARRATOR: She is ....

SECTION II: Communications in the Office

14. Taking Directions
Exercise C:

NARRATOR:
Number one. Explaining an assignment
Number two: Giving materials.

Number three: Writing deadline
Number four: Taking notes.
Number five: Making sure of details.
Number six: Highlighting information

15. Reporting Progress or Problems
Exercise C

NARRATOR: Number one.
MAN: When will you be done?

NARRATOR: Number two.
WOMAN: How's the project coming along?

NARRATOR: Number three.
MAN: There's some information missing.

NARRATOR: Number four.
WOMAN: Will you be done on time?

NARRATOR: Number five.
MAN: Which of these is correct?

16. Attending a Meeting
Exercise C

NARRATOR:
Number one: Let's get started.
Number two: Okay. Now for the next issue.
Number three: First we should talk about ....
Number four: A: No. It won't work. B: Well, it can if we want it to.
Number five: As this graph shows ....

17. Taking Minutes
Exercise C

NARRATOR: Number one.
WOMAN: Could you say that again, please?

NARRATOR: Number two.
MAN: Okay, so I'll change 16 to 60. Anything else?

NARRATOR: Number three.
WOMAN: That sounds just like a story I heard as a child.

NARRATOR: Number four.
MAN: All in favor?

NARRATOR: Number five.
WOMAN (speaking to self): Let's see. The meeting is ending at 3:30.

18. Writing a Memo
Exercise C

NARRATOR:
Number one: Tina typed the memo using her word

processing ....
Number two: She proofread the memo for ....
Number three: Near the bottom of the memo, she added ....
Number four: After Tina made copies of the memo, she ....

19. Leaving an Informal Note
Exercise C

NARRATOR:
Number one: Signing initials.
Number two: Adding the time.
Number three: Picking up a notepad.
Number four: Sticking the note.
Number five: Peeling off a piece of paper.
Number six: Jotting down a note.

REVIEW EXERCISES - Section II

Exercise D

NARRATOR: Number one.
MAN: I think I can be done by Thursday or Friday.
NARRATOR: He is ....

NARRATOR: Number two.
WOMAN: Okay, let's get started. Any amendments to the minutes?
NARRATOR: She is ....

NARRATOR: Number three.
MAN 1: It's a good idea.
WOMAN: But can we afford it?
MAN 2: Jim, what would it cost?
NARRATOR: They are ....

NARRATOR: Number four.
WOMAN (whispering): This is a really boring meeting.
MAN (whispering): Yeah.
NARRATOR: They are ....

NARRATOR: Number five.
MAN 1: Okay with me.
WOMAN: I'm for it.
MAN 2: Sure.
NARRATOR: They are ....

NARRATOR: Number six.
WOMAN: Chuck, I need to get a sales report from you. About 3 pages, covering the last 6 months.
NARRATOR: She is ....

| SECTION III: Handling Printed Materials | REVIEW EXERCISES - Section III |

SECTION III: Handling Printed Materials

20. Making Photocopies
Exercise C

NARRATOR:
Number one: I lifted it up.
Number two: I reduced it.
Number three: I adjusted it.
Number four: I placed it on the glass.

21. Dealing with Photocopier Problems
Exercise C

NARRATOR:
Number one: I fixed the copier, so now it ....
Number two: I could see that the machine was ready, because I looked at ....
Number three: The glass has some smudges on it, so I have to ....
Number four: To turn the rollers I have to ....

22. Collating and Stapling
Exercise C

NARRATOR:
Number one: The stapler's empty, so I should ....
Number two: I'm collating pages. After I pick them up, I should ....
Number three: 1, 2, 3, 4, 5. He is ....
Number four: My fingers are dry, so I'll ....

23. Keeping Pages Together/ Punching & Binding
Exercise C

NARRATOR:
Number one: It made three holes in the paper.
Number two: He put a rubber band around it.
Number three: The holes were at the edge.
Number four: The label was on the spine.

24. Filing Documents
Exercise C

NARRATOR:
Number one: We didn't have a file for him so I had to ....
Number two: I put the Ford folder before the Gibson folder. I ....
Number three: I put a file back in the drawer, so I ....
Number four: Our drawers of files are in ....

REVIEW EXERCISES - Section III

Exercise D

NARRATOR: Number one.
MAN: I have all the pages of this document.
NARRATOR: He has ....

NARRATOR: Number two.
WOMAN: I'm putting the pages out on the table. Here's page one and next to it is page two, then page three.
NARRATOR: She is ....

NARRATOR: Number three.
MAN: I'm putting a paper clip at the corner of this set of papers.
NARRATOR: He is ....

NARRATOR: Number four.
WOMAN: I'm taking away the smudges and streaks so I get better copies.
NARRATOR: She is ....

NARRATOR: Number five.
MAN: There are no more staples in the stapler, so I'm putting more in.
NARRATOR: He is ....

NARRATOR: Number six.
WOMAN: The machine has broken down.
NARRATOR: The machine ....

SECTION IV: Postal/Express Mailing

25. Receiving and Distributing Mail
Exercise C

NARRATOR:
Number one: The envelope was too big for the mail slot so Matt ....
Number two: Alice tossed the junk mail into the ....
Number three: Matt removed the letter from the envelope and ....
Number four: Alice attached the enclosure with a ....
Number five: The mail clerk arrived with the ....
Number six: Matt gave the mail clerk his ....

26. Preparing Items to be Mailed
Exercise C

NARRATOR:
Number one: She stapled it to the letter.
Number two: He proofread it.
Number three: He sealed it.
Number four: She put it in the envelope with the letter.
Number five: He corrected it.
Number six: She taped it shut.

27. Putting on Postage/Sending out Mail
Exercise C

NARRATOR:
Number one: Albert weighed a thick package.
Number two: He put the sticky label on the parcel.
Number three: She pressed the buttons on the postage meter.
Number four: Alice put her mail in the outgoing basket.
Number five: The rate chart gave the correct postage.
Number six: Albert gave the envelope to the mail clerk.

28. Using an Express Delivery Service
Exercise C

NARRATOR:
Number one: I'd like to request a package pickup, please.
Number two: Hmm. 9.5 pounds.
Number three: My tracking number is 100359.
Number four: Well, this should keep them from moving.
Number five: Let's see. Five pounds, overnight to Los Angeles. $15.

29. Receiving an Express Package
Exercise C

NARRATOR:
Number one: Albert opened the box and removed the ....
Number two: When the package arrived, Tina ....
Number three: When Tina's package was late, she called the delivery company to ....
Number four: Albert made sure nothing in the package was ....

REVIEW EXERCISES - Section IV

Exercise D

NARRATOR: Number one.
MAN: I'd better add more styrofoam peanuts before I seal this.
NARRATOR: The man is ....

NARRATOR: Number two.
WOMAN: Let's see how much this weighs.
NARRATOR: The woman is using a ....

NARRATOR: Number three.
MAN: Hello. My package was supposed to arrive yesterday and I still don't have it.
WOMAN: I'll see if I can trace it.
NARRATOR: The man and woman are talking about ....

NARRATOR: Number four.
WOMAN: Oops. Here's an error. I'd better correct it.
NARRATOR: The woman is ....

NARRATOR: Number five.
MAN: Would you like two-day or overnight delivery?
WOMAN: Overnight, please.
NARRATOR: The woman is requesting ....

NARRATOR: Number six.
MAN: Okay. Ms. Bao's mail goes here, Mr. Johnson's mail is here, and this stack is for Ms. Perez.
NARRATOR: The man is ....

SECTION V: Using Telephones and Faxes

30. Finding Telephone Numbers
Exercise C

NARRATOR:
Number one: Albert looked up a number in the phone book.
Number two: Tina asked the directory assistance operator for a listing.
Number three: Albert searched the Internet for the number he needed.
Number four: Tina flipped through her rotary file.
Number five: Albert checked his address book for a long distance number.

31. Answering a Telephone Call
Exercise C

NARRATOR:
Number one: Giving one's name.
Number two: Picking up the receiver.
Number three: Pushing down the phone line button.
Number four: Listening and taking notes.
Number five: Flashing phone line.
Number six: Hanging up the phone.

32. Making a Telephone Call
Exercise C

NARRATOR:
Number one: Is Ms Lee in?
Number two: Let's see. 9-5-2-9-2 ....
Number three: Good afternoon. Mr. Johnson's office.
Number four: Ah. Here it is. King, Robert ....
  6-5-1 ....
Number five: I'm calling about the marketing report.
Number six: This is Albert Turner from Denstar.

33. Transferring Calls
Exercise C

NARRATOR:
Number one: Before he transferred the call, Matt put the caller ....
Number two: Matt dialed Tina's ....
Number three: Albert found Matt's extension ....
Number four: Albert put the caller on hold. Next he ....
Number five: When Tina answered, Matt announced ....
Number six: Matt put the caller on hold by ....

34. Taking a Message
Exercise C

NARRATOR:
Number one: Hello. Is Alice Bao in?
Number two: Can you spell your last name, please?
Number three: May I take a message?
Number four: Sales. This is Albert Turner.
Number five: May I have your phone number?

35. Leaving a Message
Exercise C

NARRATOR:
Number one: Alice left a message on the answering machine.
Number two: The secretary said Ms. Martin was not available.
Number three: Matt thanked the secretary and said goodbye.
Number four: He asked if Alice wanted to leave a message.

36. Sending a Fax
Exercise C

NARRATOR:
Number one: Albert loaded the document in the fax machine ....
Number two: Albert dialed the fax number of the ....
Number three: When the machine was ready, Albert pressed the ....
Number four: The display on the machine showed ....
Number five: After the fax was sent, Albert removed the pages from the ....
Number six: The pages feed into the machine ....

37. Receiving a Fax
Exercise C

NARRATOR:
Number one: Removing pages from the tray.
Number two: Pages are entering the document receive tray.

Number three: The display is showing an incoming fax.
Number four: Tina is delivering the fax to its recipient.
Number five: The fax machine is beeping.
Number six: Tina is checking for missing pages.

38. Dealing with Fax Machine Problems
Exercise C

NARRATOR:
Number one: It said the paper was jammed.
Number two: Albert pushed on it and it closed.
Number three: He put pages in it to send a fax.
Number four: It was empty so Tina refilled it.
Number five: Alice replaced it with a new one.
Number six: Albert looked in it when he had a problem.

REVIEW EXERCISES - Section V

Exercise D

NARRATOR: Number one.
WOMAN: Let's see. Lee, Ann .... Lee, Charles .... Here it is. Donald Lee, 9-5-2 ....
NARRATOR: The woman is ....

NARRATOR: Number two.
MAN: This is George Davis from Indent Corporation. Could you please tell Ms. Perez I called?
NARRATOR: The man is ....

NARRATOR: Number three.
WOMAN: Hello Mr. Johnson. This is Linda Smith. I've got a question about tomorrow's meeting.
NARRATOR: She is ....

NARRATOR: Number four.
MAN: Hello. United Software.
WOMAN: Hello. This is Janet Timson from UniData Incorporated.
NARRATOR: The woman is ....

NARRATOR: Number five.
MAN: I'll get this ready then fax the document.
NARRATOR: The man is ....

NARRATOR: Number six.
Woman: Jim, I can't read this fax. The print is too light.
MAN: Oh, I can help you.
NARRATOR: The man is going to ....

SECTION VI: Using Computers and Other Office Machines

39. Starting a Computer
Exercise C

NARRATOR:

Number one: Using his foot, Matt pressed the button on the ....

Number two: After Matt turned on his monitor, the cursor began ....

Number three: Icons appeared on the ....

Number four: Tina moved the pointer with the ....

Number five: She clicked on ....

Number six: Tina opened the ....

40. Shutting Down a Computer
Exercise C

NARRATOR:

Number one: It went dark.

Number two: Albert saved it.

Number three: He turned it off with his foot.

Number four: It asked if he wanted to shut down.

Number five: Albert chose it from the menu.

Number six: It shut off.

41. Keying in Text
Exercise C

NARRATOR:

Number one: Tina pressed the enter key.

Number two: Matt typed on the keyboard.

Number three: Matt opened the word processing program.

Number four: Tina saved the report.

Number five: Matt indented the new line with the tab key.

Number six: Tina checked the spelling.

42. Printing
Exercise C

NARRATOR:

Number one: Albert removed the copy from the output tray.

Number two: Albert added paper to the feeder.

Number three: Albert turned on his printer.

Number four: He printed a copy.

Number five: Albert previewed the document.

Number six: He set up the print job.

43. Receiving E-mail
Exercise C

NARRATOR:

Number one: Several new messages were listed in Matt's ....

Number two: Alice deleted the message because it was ....

Number three: To open his e-mail program, Matt entered his ....

Number four: After Alice read the message, she replied to the ....

Number five: To open the message, Alice ....

Number six: After Alice read the last message she ....

44. Sending E-mail
Exercise C

NARRATOR:

Number one: Tina is starting her e-mail program.

Number two: Tina is opening her e-mail address book.

Number three: Tina is attaching a file to her message.

Number four: Tina is scrolling through the list of names in her address book.

Number five: Tina is exiting her e-mail program.

Number six: A message told Tina her mail had been sent.

45. Getting Information from the Internet
Exercise C

NARRATOR:

Number one: I type this in to start a search.

Number two: After I exited my browser I did this.

Number three: One of the hits looked interesting so I did this.

Number four: A link looked interesting, so I did this.

46. Using a Typewriter
Exercise C

NARRATOR:

Number one: Albert set it.

Number two: He turned it clockwise.

Number three: He pressed it to make an uppercase letter.

Number four: Albert turned it on.

Number five: He put a piece of paper in it.

Number six: He pressed it and fed the paper into the machine.

47. Using a Calculator
Exercise C

NARRATOR:

Number one: Alice entered the numbers on the calculator ....

Number two: Matt subtracted the number using the ....

Number three: As Alice added the receipts, the numbers appeared on the ....

Number four: Matt discovered an incorrect number so he ....

Number five: When Matt was done, he tore off the ....

Number six: When Alice was finished, she totaled the ....

Exercise D

NARRATOR: Number one.
WOMAN: Well, it's almost time to go so I'd better save this document.
NARRATOR: The woman is ....

NARRATOR: Number two.
MAN: Oh, I didn't notice all these mistakes. I'd better correct them.
NARRATOR: The man is ....

NARRATOR: Number three.
WOMAN: Let's see. I think I'll preview the document first. Hmm. Everything looks ready to go.
NARRATOR: The woman is going to ....

NARRATOR: Number four.
MAN: Hmm. This message looks interesting. I'd better send this on to Ms. Perez.
NARRATOR: The man is going to ....

NARRATOR: Number five.
WOMAN: Can you please show me how this works?
MAN: Sure. Just feed the paper in with the return key and straighten it. Okay. Now it's ready.
NARRATOR: The man is explaining how to use a ....

NARRATOR: Number six.
WOMAN: Time to add up these receipts. Let's see, 572 plus 873 plus 650 ....
NARRATOR: The woman is ....

SECTION VII: Money Matters

48. Receiving an Invoice/Paying
Exercise C

NARRATOR:
Number one: It was in the package that was delivered.
Number two: Albert compared it to the invoice.
Number three: Albert issued it.
Number four: It was delivered.
Number five: He stamped "paid" on it.
Number six: He attached the check to it.

49. Issuing a Check
Exercise C

NARRATOR:
Number one: The payee is Brown Software. The date is August 6, 2002. The amount of the check is $215.25.

Number two: The payee is A to Z Computers. The date is December 8, 2002. The amount of the check is $675.50.

50. Sending Out a Bill
Exercise C

NARRATOR:
Number one: Alice prepared an invoice for a ....
Number two: She reviewed the items on the ....
Number three: She double-checked the amount ....
Number four: She printed three copies of the ....
Number five: She put a copy of the invoice and purchase order in the customer's ....
Number six: She sent the invoices to the ....

51. Receiving Payment
Exercise C

NARRATOR:
Number one: Matt opened this to record the payment.
Number two: He did this on the back of the check.
Number three: He stamped this on the invoice.
Number four: He posted this in the accounts receivable file.
Number five: Matt put the check in this.
Number six: When he was finished, he filed this.

52. Working with Petty Cash
Exercise C

NARRATOR:
Number one: The manager is approving the voucher.
Number two: Matt is attaching the voucher and receipt.
Number three: Alice is bringing a receipt for reimbursement.
Number four: Matt is filling out a petty cash voucher.
Number five: Alice is signing the voucher.
Number six: Matt is counting out Alice's reimbursement.

Exercise D

NARRATOR: Number one.
WOMAN: Hi Joe. Here's the receipt for the beverages I bought for the office party.
MAN: Okay. Let's just fill out this form for your reimbursement.
NARRATOR: They are going to complete ....

NARRATOR: Number two.
MAN: Excuse me, Ms. Perez. Could you review and sign this voucher, please?
WOMAN: Sure (Pause) Here you go.
MAN: Thank you.
NARRATOR: The woman ....

NARRATOR: Number three.
MAN: Let's see. Payee, Omega Software. (Pause) Amount, $560 ....
NARRATOR: The man is ....

NARRATOR: Number four.
WOMAN: I'd better enter this customer's payment.
NARRATOR: The woman is going to ....

NARRATOR: Number five.
MAN: I'd better look at the purchase order and invoice and make sure everything looks okay.
NARRATOR: The man is going to ....

SECTION VIII: Maintaining the Office

53. Getting Supplies from a Stockroom
Exercise C

NARRATOR:
Number one: He filled out a form to order more disks.
Number two: He opened the supply cabinet.
Number three: He noticed that it was the last disk.
Number four: He opened a box of file folders.
Number five: He crossed out the amount on the inventory.
Number six: He noted the new amount of paper.

54. Dealing with Accidents
Exercise C

NARRATOR:
Number one: When Matt cut his hand it was only a ....
Number two: Matt cleaned and bandaged his ....
Number three: When Matt cut his finger he got out the ....
Number four: Albert fell in the break room when he ....
Number five: Alice called the emergency number because Albert had a ....
Number six: The paramedics brought Albert to the ....

55. Handling Maintenance Problems
Exercise C

NARRATOR:
Number one: Could you send someone to clean up a spill?
Number two: Hello. We have a broken water pipe in our office.
Number three: Hi. One of our lights is burned out.
Number four: I don't think the air conditioning is working.
Number five: There. Your air conditioning is fixed.

56. Handling Office Security
Exercise C

NARRATOR:
Number one: Before Matt shredded the documents, he removed the ....
Number two: Matt emptied the shredded paper into the ....
Number three: After Tina punched in the code, the alarm was ....
Number four: The guard saw the unfamiliar person on the security ....
Number five: The guard escorted the unwanted visitor ....
Number six: Tina keeps her purse ....

REVIEW EXERCISES - Section VIII

Exercise D

NARRATOR: Number one
MAN: Hey! There's a problem with this light.
WOMAN: I just called maintenance. Someone's coming to replace it.
NARRATOR: The man and woman are talking about a ....

NARRATOR: Number two.
WOMAN: Hello. One of my co-workers fell and injured his leg. Could you send the paramedics, please?
NARRATOR: The woman is ....

NARRATOR: Number three.
WOMAN: Say, Bob, I just noticed there's only one box of paper left in the supply cabinet.
MAN: Thanks for telling me. I'll order more.
NARRATOR: The man is going to ....

NARRATOR: Number four.
WOMAN: Excuse me. I just saw a suspicious woman in the office workroom.
MAN: We've had security problems lately. I'd better go find her.
NARRATOR: They are talking about ....

NARRATOR: Number five.
MAN: I just need to punch in the code and then I can leave. Let's see, 5 .... 8 .... 0 .... 1. That's it.
NARRATOR: The man just ....

81

ANSWER KEY

SECTION I: Daily Routines

1. Getting Ready for Work

A
1. putting on
2. watching
3. getting dressed
4. making
5. packing
6. shutting

B
1. c
2. e
3. b
4. f
5. d
6. a

C
1. briefcase
2. a brown bag
3. casual clothes
4. dress clothes
5. laundry
6. a shower

2. Arriving at the Office

A
1. parking
2. walking
3. making small talk
4. taking
5. hanging
6. entering
7. going through
8. unlocking

B
1. building
2. parking lot
3. hall
4. office cubicle

C.
1. a door
2. an elevator
3. a key
4. coworkers
5. her briefcase
6. a parking lot

3. Going through Security

A
1. entering
2. letting
3. checking
4. temporary pass
5. restricted
6. identifying

B
1. wave
2. ID
3. badge
4. recognize
5. number

C
1. b
2. a
3. f
4. d
5. e
6. c

4. Reporting for Work

A
1. moving something
2. writing in a time
3. punching in
4. putting something in

B
1. showed
2. took
3. moved
4. opened
5. wrote in
6. check
7. punched in
8. printed

C
1. was in
2. punched in
3. the clock
4. the rack
5. printed
6. opened
7. column
8. name

5. Getting Settled at the Office

A
1. d
2. e
3. f
4. a
5. b
6. c

B
1. at
2. on
3. in
4. from
5. at
6. to

C
a. 3
b. 8
c. 5
d. 2
e. 6
f. 4
g. 1
h. 7

6. Planning Your Day/Scheduling

A
1. date book
2. electronic organizer
3. desk calendar
4. to-do list

B
1. software
2. date book
3. find out
4. conflicts

C
1. has an appointment
2. penciled in
3. schedule conflict
4. reschedule

7. Checking Voicemail Messages

A
1. picking up
2. entering
3. pressing
4. listening to
5. writing
6. hanging up

B
1. c
2. f
3. a
4. e
5. b
6. d

C
1. deleted it
2. replayed it
3. saved it
4. missed the beginning
5. exited voicemail
6. wrote down the caller's name

8. Taking a Coffee Break

A
1. c
2. d
3. f
4. a
5. e
6. b

B
1. notice
2. breakroom
3. coin slot
4. change
5. bin
6. up

C
1. offering a snack
2. making small talk
3. counting out money
4. looking at a bulletin board
5. looking at a vending machine
6. returning to work

9. Eating Lunch in a Cafeteria

A
1. c   3. f   5. d
2. e   4. a   6. b

B
1. security   4. lettuce
2. tongs   5. security
3. napkin   guard

C
a. 3   d. 2   g. 8
b. 5   e. 1   h. 7
c. 6   f. 4

10. Eating a Bag Lunch

A
1. f   3. b   5. c
2. e   4. a   6. d

B
1. Alice took the container out of the microwave.
2. Matt wrapped up his sandwich.
3. Alice set the timer on the microwave.
4. Alice loosened the cover.
5. Matt poured some tea from his vacuum bottle.
6. Matt took a bite of his sandwich.

C
1. refrigerator
2. microwave
3. vacuum bottle
4. threw it away
5. container
6. loosened the lid

11. Spending Lunchtime in Other Ways

A
1. gym   4. locker room
2. errands   5. cards
3. tip   6. cigarette

B
1. e   3. f   5. d
2. c   4. a   6. b

C
1. ordering lunch
2. mailing a package
3. making a personal call
4. going to the bank
5. using exercise equipment
6. shopping

12. Ending the Workday

A
1. printing   4. returning
2. crossing off   5. locking
3. putting   6. turning off

B
1. d   3. e   5. c
2. f   4. a   6. b

C
1. shut off   4. lights
2. looked at   5. locked
3. file

13. Leaving the Office

A
1. d   3. b   5. f
2. c   4. a   6. e

B
1. moving   3. setting
2. writing   4. putting

C
1. book   4. time
2. signed out   5. board
3. found   6. line

Review Exercises - Section I

A
1. their names
2. some sun
3. a PIN
4. some small talk
5. a meal
6. swimming
7. good morning

B
1. ordering   6. taking
2. entering   7. writing
3. pressing   8. making
4. putting   9. signing
5. packing

C
1. c   5. g   9. e
2. h   6. j   10. f
3. a   7. d
4. b   8. i

D
1. Their break is up.
2. recognize her
3. dropping something off
4. making small talk
5. counting
6. ordering something

Section II: Communications in the Office

14. Taking Directions

A
1. f   3. a   5. b
2. e   4. d   6. c

B
1. files   3. nodded
2. deadline   4. highlighted

C
a. 3   c. 1   e. 4
b. 6   d. 5   f. 2

15. Reporting Progress or Problems

A
1. pointing   4. left
2. progress   5. explaining
3. estimating   6. meeting

B
1. d   3. f   5. b
2. c   4. a   6. e

C
1. c   3. e   5. d
2. a   4. b

16. Attending a Meeting

A
1. taking up   4. making
2. taking   5. distributing
3. thanking   6. giving

B
1. c   3. b   5. f
2. e   4. d   6. a

C
1. opening a meeting
2. moving on to the next item
3. taking up the first item of business
4. discussing something
5. giving a presentation

17. Taking Minutes

A
1. d   4. g   7. f
2. c   5. h   8. a
3. e   6. b

B
1. summarize   4. Minutes
2. for the record   5. record
3. amend   6. Remarks

C
1. b   3. e   5. d
2. c   4. a

18. Writing a Memo

A
1. opening   4. proofreading
2. typing up   5. showing
3. printing out   6. distributing

B
1. date   4. subject
2. recipient list   5. body
3. sender's name   6. typist's initials

C
1. software   3. her initials
2. mistakes   4. distributed it

19. Leaving an Informal Note

A
1. b   3. c   5. a
2. f   4. d   6. e

B
1. initials   3. self-adhesive
2. away   4. message

C
a. 5   c. 3   e. 4
b. 1   d. 6   f. 2

Review Exercises - Section II

A
1. the time   5. a coworker for help
2. the floor
3. a message   6. a supervisor
4. the last meeting   7. the first item of business

B
1. nodding   5. explaining
2. peeling   6. pointing out
3. typing   7. yawning
4. reporting

C
1. i   5. e   8. b
2. c   6. a   9. d
3. j   7. g   10. f
4. h

D
1. estimating
2. opening a meeting
3. discussing something
4. whispering
5. approving something
6. explaining an assignment

Section III: Handling Printed Materials

20. Making Photocopies

A
1. d   3. a   5. b
2. c   4. e   6. f

B
1. face-down   4. sorted
2. crosswise   5. cleared
3. face-up   6. multi-page

C
1. lid   3. settings
2. size   4. document

21. Dealing with Photocopier Problems

A
1. pulling   4. working
2. putting   5. broke
3. see   6. reaching

B
1. jam
2. it's running now
3. toolboxes
4. reaching inside

C
1. works again   3. clean it
2. the display   4. turn a knob

22. Collating and Stapling

A
1. d   3. b   5. e
2. c   4. f   6. a

B
1. laid out   3. upper right
2. out of   4. on top of

C
1. reload it
2. put one on top of another
3. counting sets
4. lick them

23. Keeping Pages Together/ Punching & Binding

A
1. d   3. e   5. b
2. f   4. a   6. c

B
1. aligning   3. slipping
2. side-stapling   4. emptying

C
1. three holes   3. edge
2. rubber   4. spine

24. Filing Documents

A
1. f   3. c   5. b
2. e   4. a   6. d

B
1. on   3. about
2. through   4. larger

C
1. set up a new one
2. arranged them alphabetically
3. re-filed it
4. a filing cabinet

Review Exercises - Section III

A
1. a sheet
2. a repair service
3. the display of a copier
4. the settings darker
5. one sheet on top of another

B
1. pressing   2. stacking

3. entering   6. putting
4. turning   7. laying
5. licking

C
1. e   5. i   8. c
2. h   6. a   9. b
3. j   7. f   10. g
4. d

D
1. a full set
2. putting the pages in order
3. clipping the pages together
4. cleaning the glass
5. reloading a stapler
6. doesn't work

Section IV:
Postal/Express Mailing

25. Receiving and Distributing Mail

A
1. e   3. a   5. d
2. c   4. f   6. b

B
1. An enclosure   4. Outgoing mail
2. Junk mail   5. Incoming mail
3. Confidential   6. Interoffice
   mail   mail

C
1. folded it   4. paper clip
2. recycle bin   5. mail cart
3. unfolded it   6. outgoing mail

26. Preparing Items to be Mailed

A
1. addressing   5. correcting
2. proofreading   6. stapling
3. sealing   7. typing
4. adding   8. putting

B
1. draft   3. attachments
2. address label   4. proofreading

C
1. attachment   4. the enclosure
2. the draft   5. the error
3. the envelope   6. the package

27. Putting on Postage/ Sending out Mail

A
1. moistened   4. postage meter
2. postage scale   5. display
3. amount

B
1. e   3. d   5. f
2. c   4. a   6. b

C
1. package   4. basket
2. sticky   5. chart
3. meter   6. mail clerk

28. Using an Express Delivery Service

A
1. c   3. e   5. f
2. d   4. a   6. b

B
1. putting   5. sticking
2. sealing   6. bringing
3. measuring   7. checking
4. filling out 8. giving

C
1. calling a delivery service
2. weighing a package
3. checking the status of a package
4. adding packing material
5. checking delivery prices

29. Receiving an Express Package

A
1. f   3. e   5. b
2. c   4. a   6. d

B
1. damaged   4. late
2. fill out /   5. tracking
   claim form   number
3. lost, trace   6. make sure

C
1. contents   3. report it
2. signed for it 4. damaged

Review Exercises - Section IV

A
1. an outgoing basket

2. a stamp
3. postage from rate charts
4. a slot to a postage meter
5. a delivery person
6. stamps
7. a postage label on the scale

B
1. folding   5. sorting
2. handing   6. stamping
3. weighing   7. addressing
4. signing for   8. attaching

C
1. d   5. j   8. c
2. g   6. b   9. h
3. e   7. i   10. a
4. f

D
1. packing a box
2. scale
3. a lost package
4. proofreading a letter
5. delivery service
6. sorting mail

Section V: Using Telephones and Faxes

30. Finding Telephone Numbers

A
1. flipping   4. giving
   through   5. searching
2. running   6. looking in
3. dialing

B
1. c   3. b   5. a
2. d   4. f   6. e

C
1. looked up   4. file
2. listing   5. long distance
3. Internet

31. Answering a Telephone Call

A
1. d   3. e   5. f
2. b   4. c   6. a

B
1. identified   4. pushed
2. said hello   5. reason
3. flashed   6. said goodbye

C
a. 2   c. 4   e. 5
b. 1   d. 6   f. 3

32. Making a Telephone Call

A
1. dial tone   4. secretary
2. directory   5. explain
3. open

B
1. d   3. a   5. b
2. c   4. f   6. e

C
1. asking to speak to someone
2. dialing a phone number
3. a secretary answering the phone
4. looking up a phone number
5. a caller explaining why he called
6. a caller identifying himself

33. Transferring Calls

A
1. dialing   4. looking up
2. putting   5. announcing
3. pushing   6. hanging up

B
1. e   3. d   5. b
2. f   4. a   6. c

C
1. on hold
2. extension
3. in the directory
4. pushed the transfer button
5. the call
6. pushing the button

34. Taking a Message

A
1. d   3. c   5. b
2. f   4. e   6. a

B
1. for
2. date and time
3. caller
4. telephone number
5. message

C
1. b   3. d   5. c
2. e   4. a

35. Leaving a Message

A
1. asking   5. returns
2. leave   6. explaining
3. spelling   7. telling
4. giving   8. thanking

B
1. d   3. a
2. b   4. c

C
a. answering   c. thanked
   machine   d. message
b. available

36. Sending a Fax

A
1. one by one   4. sender
2. face down   5. scans
3. addressee   6. cover sheet

B
1. d   3. e   5. a
2. b   4. c   6. f

C
1. face down   4. ready
2. addressee   5. tray
3. send button   6. one by one

37. Receiving a Fax

A
1. f   3. c   5. d
2. e   4. a   6. b

B
1. display   4. missing
2. entered   5. stapled
3. checked   6. recipient

C
a. 6   c. 5   e. 3
b. 2   d. 4   f. 1

38. Dealing with Fax Machine Problems

A
1. jammed   4. replacing
2. opening   5. looking at
3. separating   6. calling

B
1. e   4. d   7. h
2. a   5. f   8. c
3. b   6. g

C
1. b   3. c   5. d
2. a   4. e   6. f

Review Exercises - Section IV

A
1. flipping   6. loading
2. dialing   7. removing
3. hanging up   8. refilling
4. looking up   9. writing down
5. spelling

B
1. rotary file   4. fax tone
2. an area code   5. receiving
3. problem   6. document

C
1. g   5. h   8. c
2. e   6. i   9. d
3. a   7. b   10. j
4. f

D
1. looking up a number
2. leaving a message
3. explaining why she called
4. identifying herself
5. preparing a cover sheet
6. replace the ink cartridge

Section VI: Using Computers and Other Office Machines

39. Starting a Computer

A
1. e   3. a   5. c
2. d   4. f   6. b

B
1. icon   3. flashes
2. mouse pad   4. button

C
1. power strip   4. mouse
2. flashing   5. an icon
3. screen   6. program

40. Shutting Down A Computer

A
1. b   3. a   5. c
2. e   4. d

B
1. saving   4. asking
2. closing   5. shut down
3. choosing   6. turned off

C
1. c   3. e   5. f
2. b   4. d   6. a

41. Keying in Text

A
1. indent   5. space
2. capital   6. enter
3. tab   7. delete
4. Boldface   8. shift

B
1. g   4. e   6. f
2. b   5. c   7. d
3. a

C
1. enter   4. saved
2. keyboard   5. tab
3. opened   6. spelling

42. Printing

A
1. set up   4. power light
2. feeder   5. paper guides
3. preview   6. output tray

B
1. e   3. f   5. d
2. c   4. a   6. b

C
a. 1   c. 3   e. 2
b. 5   d. 6   f. 4

43. Receiving E-mail

A
1. opening   5. closing
2. entering   6. saving
3. deleting   7. replying
4. double-clicking 8. exiting

B
1. c   3. e   5. a
2. f   4. d   6. b

C
1. inbox
2. junk mail
3. password
4. sender
5. double-clicked on it
6. exited her e-mail program

44. Sending E-mail

A
1. d   3. e   5. a
2. b   4. f   6. c

B
a. 2   c. 1
b. 3   d. 4

C
a. 6   c. 1   e. 5
b. 2   d. 3   f. 4

45. Getting Information from the Internet

A
1. f   3. b   5. a
2. e   4. c   6. d

B
1. pointer   3. typing
2. listed   4. link

C
1. a keyword   3. clicked on it
2. went off line 4. followed it

46. Using a Typewriter

A
1. c   4. d   7. h
2. f   5. a   8. e
3. b   6. i   9. g

B
1. paper
2. platen
3. securing the paper
4. straighten the keys

C
1. a   3. e   5. b
2. c   4. f   6. d

47. Using a Calculator

A
1. entering   5. printing
2. feeding   6. totaling
3. adding   7. tearing
4. subtracting 8. clearing

B
1. e   4. a   7. f
2. g   5. d   8. c
3. h   6. b

C
1. keypad   4. subtracted it
2. minus key   5. printout
3. display   6. results

Review Exercises - Section VI

A
1. clicking on   7. straightening
2. typing   8. subtracting
3. turning off   9. closing
4. turning   10. moving
5. printing   11. pulling
6. scrolling   12. clearing

B
1. a recipient's 4. the printer
   name   5. an enter key
2. a password   6. a printer
3. a mouse

C
1. c   5. j   8. b
2. e   6. a   9. h
3. f   7. i   10. d
4. g

D
1. using a word processing program
2. checking the spelling
3. print a document
4. forward a message
5. typewriter
6. entering numbers

Section VII: Money Matters

48. Receiving an Invoice/Paying

A
1. record   3. Confirm,
2. invoice   make sure

4. detail   6. order
5. issue a check

B
1. d   3. e   5. f
2. c   4. b   6. a

C
1. b   3. a   5. f
2. e   4. d   6. c

49. Issuing a Check

A
1. writing out   5. opening
2. stub   6. payee
3. tearing out   7. clicking on
4. signing   8. printed

B
1. d   3. f   5. c
2. b   4. e   6. a

C
1. Date: August 6 2002
   Payee: Brown Software
   Amount: Two hundred and
   fifteen and 25/100 dollars or
   $215.25
2. Date: December 8 2002
   Payee: A to Z Computers
   Amount: Six hundred and
   seventy-five and 50/100 dollars
   or $675.50

50. Sending Out a Bill

A
1. double-check   4. prepare
2. bill   5. customer
3. due   6. overdue

B
1. d   3. a   5. b
2. f   4. c   6. e

C
1. customer   4. invoice
2. purchase   5. file
   order   6. customer
3. due

51. Receiving Payment

A
1. d   3. b   5. c
2. a   4. f   6. e

B
1. recording   4. stamping
2. endorsing   5. placing
3. posting   6. filing

C
1. accounts   4. the payment
   receivable file   5. the safe
2. endorsed it   6. the invoice
3. paid

52. Working with Petty Cash

A
1. b   3. a   5. f
2. c   4. e   6. d

B
1. reimburse-   4. counted
   ment   5. signed
2. petty cash   6. carbon copy
3. unlocked

C
a. 6   c. 3   e. 2
b. 1   d. 4   f. 5

Review Exercises - Section VII

A
1. comparing   7. filing
2. signing   8. entering
3. separating   9. mailing
4. endorsing   10. filling out
5. stamping   11. unlocking
6. recording   12. counting

B
1. open it   4. the total
2. stamp   amount due
3. tear it   5. print it

C
1. h   5. j   8. e
2. i   6. d   9. f
3. b   7. g   10. a
4. c

D
1. a petty cash voucher
2. approved the voucher
3. issuing a check
4. post a payment
5. compare the purchase order and
   invoice

Section VIII: Maintaining the Office

53. Getting Supplies from a Stockroom

1. inventory   4. note
2. requisition   5. on hand
3. Amount   6. supply room

B
1. e   3. a   5. f
2. c   4. d   6. b

C
1. order   4. opened
2. supply   5. crossed out
   cabinet   6. noted
3. noticed

54. Dealing with Accidents

A
1. fell   5. completed
2. injured   6. cut
3. emergency   7. first aid kit
   number   8. bandaged
4. paramedics

B
1. c   3. b   5. a
2. d   4. e

C
1. minor injury   5. serious
2. wound   accident
3. first aid kit   6. hospital
4. slipped

55. Handling Maintenance Problems

A
1. burned out   5. mopped up
2. changed   6. noticed
3. spill   7. problem
4. building   8. replaced
   maintenance

B
1. d   4. g   6. c
2. f   5. e   7. a
3. b

C
1. d   3. a   5. b
2. e   4. c

56.   Handling Office Security

A
1. confidential
2. precaution
3. out of sight
4. activated
5. mumbles
6. alarm
7. shred
8. escort

B
1. b
2. d
3. a
4. f
5. c
6. e

C
1. paper clips
2. recycle bin
3. activated
4. screen
5. out of the building
6. out of sight

Review Exercises - Section VIII

A
1. opening
2. shredding
3. escorting
4. replacing
5. crossing out
6. punching
7. fixing
8. bandaging
9. calling

B
1. guards
2. reams of paper
3. falls
4. paramedics
5. mop up spills

C
1. c
2. d
3. g
4. e
5. j
6. a
7. b
8. i
9. f
10. h

D
1. burned out bulb
2. calling an emergency number
3. fill out a requisition form
4. an unwanted visitor
5. activated the alarm